Hardening, Tempering, Annealing
AND FORGING OF STEEL

A Treatise on the Practical Treatment and Working
of High and Low Grade Steel

COMPRISING

THE SELECTION AND IDENTIFICATION OF STEEL, THE MOST
MODERN AND APPROVED HEATING, HARDENING, TEMPERING,
ANNEALING AND FORGING PROCESSES, THE USE OF GAS BLAST
FORGES, HEATING MACHINES AND FURNACES, THE ANNEALING
AND MANUFACTURING OF MALLEABLE IRON, THE TREAT-
MENT AND USE OF SELF-HARDENING STEEL, WITH SPECIAL
REFERENCE TO CASEHARDENING PROCESSES, THE HARDEN-
ING AND TEMPERING OF MILLING CUTTERS AND PRESS
TOOLS, THE USE OF MACHINERY STEEL FOR CUTTING TOOLS,
FORGING AND WELDING, HIGH GRADE STEEL FORGINGS IN
AMERICA, FORGING OF HOLLOW SHAFTS, DROP-FORGING,
AND GRINDING PROCESSES FOR TOOLS AND MACHINE PARTS

By

JOSEPH V. WOODWORTH

Author of "Dies, Their Construction and Use" etc., etc.

Third Edition
Fully Illustrated by 201 Engravings

New York :
THE NORMAN W. HENLEY PUBLISHING COMPANY
132 Nassau Street
1907

Hardening, Tempering, Annealing and Forging of Steel

by Joseph V. Woodworth

Originally published by
Norman W. Henley Publishing Co
New York

Reprinted by Lindsay Publications Inc
Bradley IL 60915

ISBN 1-55918-049-8

1 2 3 4 5 6 7 8 9 0

1990

TO

GEORGE WOODWORTH

MY FATHER, FRIEND AND FELLOW WORKER, TO WHOSE LOVE,
AFFECTION AND ENCOURAGEMENT I OWE MORE THAN
CAN EVER BE REPAID, THIS BOOK IS
AFFECTIONATELY DEDICATED

WARNING

Remember that the materials and methods described here are from another era. Workers were less safety conscious then, and some methods may be downright dangerous. Be careful! Use good solid judgement in your work, and think ahead. Lindsay Publications Inc. has not tested these methods and materials and does not endorse them. Our job is merely to pass along to you information from another era. Safety is your responsibility.

Write for a complete catalog of unusual books available from:

Lindsay Publications Inc
PO Box 12
Bradley IL 60915-0012

PREFACE.

In preparing this treatise the author has had as an incitement the knowledge that there was very little information to be had on the treatment and working of steel of practical value to the general mechanic. For this reason he is convinced that a practical book on the treatment and working of the metal as modern demands necessitate, that is, in regard to heating, annealing, forging, hardening and tempering processes, cannot fail to prove of interest and value to all mechanics who use tools or who are in any way engaged in the working of metals.

When the fact is considered that tools made from the best grades of steel will not perform the work required unless they have been treated properly during the various heating processes, the value of a knowledge of the most satisfactory and approved arrangements and methods to the mechanic is at once apparent.

With the object in view of giving to practical men a book treating and presenting this paramount subject in a clear, concise and practical manner, the author has drawn upon a personal experience of many years, gathered all the information obtainable, eliminating all unnecessary and obsolete matter, and added all that is approved, up-to-date and authentic.

In regard to originality we lay claim to very little, for, although the facts contained in a large number of the items have been gained through years of experience at the forge, bench and machine, we are indebted to others for a greater portion, and merely claim to have, as a great poet has said, *"gathered the fruits of other men's labors and bound them with our own string."* To the technical journals, notably the American Machinist, Machinery, the Iron Age, the Scientific American, the Age of Steel, Modern Machinery, and Shop Talk; to master mechanics of well-known shops, to many American machine-tool and tool and die making concerns, and to individual fellow craftsmen, the author takes pleasure in herein acknowledging his indebtedness, with thanks for a large number of facts contained in this volume.

The chapters on Miscellaneous Methods, Tables, and on Emery

Wheel Grinding of tools, have been thought so near akin to the general subject of this work, that they have been given a place and will be found valuable to the tool maker and general machinist.

Much valuable information was furnished, and many of the engravings which were used to illustrate the work were kindly loaned to the author by the following named firms: Cincinnati Milling Machine Company, Cincinnati, Ohio; American Gas Furnace Company, New York, N. Y.; Faneuil Watch Tool Company, Brighton, Boston, Mass.; Standard Tool Company, Cleveland, Ohio; J. H. Williams Company, Brooklyn, N. Y.; the Rogers & Hubbard Company, Middletown, Conn.; Pratt & Whitney, Hartford, Conn.; Garvin Machine Company, New York, N. Y.; Armstrong Brothers Tool Company, Chicago, Ill.; Chicago Flexible Shaft Company, Chicago, Ill.; Nicholson File Company, Providence, R. I.; E. W. Bliss Company, Brooklyn, N. Y.

Although the writer is aware that his efforts will meet with criticism from those who may feel that it is not technical enough, or that some particular process or special method has been ignored, he is pleased to assure the reader that all that it does contain has been authenticated, and he is convinced that the majority will find in its pages information which will assist them in overcoming trials and difficulties met with in the working of this *"truly wondrous metal."*

Brooklyn, N. Y.,

JOSEPH V. WOODWORTH.

CONTENTS.

CHAPTER I.

CHAPTER II.

CHAPTER III.

THE HEATING AND COOLING OF STEEL—LOCATION OF HEATING ARRANGE-
MENTS—THE USE OF GAS BLAST FURNACES AND HEATING MACHINES
—TOUGH STEEL AND HARD STEEL—THE DIFFERENCE.

CHAPTER IV.

THE HARDENING OF STEEL—HARDENING IN WATER, BRINE, OIL, AND SOLU-
TIONS—SPECIAL PROCESSES FOR SPECIAL STEEL.

CHAPTER V.

TEMPERING—BY COLORS—IN OIL—ON HOT PLATES—BY THERMOMETER—IN HOT WATER—IN THE SAND BATH—BY SPECIAL METHODS.

CHAPTER VI.

CASE-HARDENING PROCESSES—THE USE OF MACHINERY STEEL FOR CUTTING TOOLS AND THE TREATMENT OF IT.

CHAPTER VII.

HARDENING AND TEMPERING MILLING CUTTERS AND SIMILAR TOOLS.

CHAPTER VIII.

HARDENING, TEMPERING AND STRAIGHTENING ALL KINDS OF SMALL TOOLS.

CHAPTER IX.

THE HARDENING AND TEMPERING OF DIES AND ALL KINDS OF PRESS TOOLS FOR THE WORKING OF SHEET METAL.

CHAPTER X.

FORGING AND WELDING—HOW TO ACCOMPLISH SATISFACTORY RESULTS IN THE FORGING AND WELDING OF STEEL AND IRON—DROP FORGING.

CHAPTER XI.

MISCELLANEOUS METHODS, PROCESSES, KINKS, POINTERS AND TABLES FOR USE IN METAL WORKING.

CHAPTER XII.

GRINDING—THE ACCURATE AND RAPID GRINDING OF TOOLS AND SMALL
MACHINE PARTS—EMERY WHEELS—THEIR USE.

CHAPTER I.

Selection and Identification of Steel.

It would be a fine thing if we could start with giving the name of a brand of tool steel which would answer for all kinds of tools; would harden without trouble, and temper evenly in the "good old-fashioned way." But as we cannot do this, we can only hope that some day a steel which *will* answer for all purposes will be produced; until then we must rest content with what we have got and through experience learn of the best brand of steel to use for a given purpose.

There is absolutely no economy in purchasing tool steel because it is cheap. In fact, economy in steel can only be obtained by purchasing a grade of steel which is uniformly of the best quality, as its superior lasting quality, and its ability to retain a cutting edge for long periods make it the cheapest and most satisfactory in the end. Such steel costs more in the beginning, but then cheap steel has often cost almost "its weight in gold" before it was thrown out. Almost every machinist, who has worked in any number of shops, has had experience with the different grades and brands of steel for tools, and he knows that cheap steel *is* expensive.

As the first thing necessary to allow of successful metal working, in any branch of the machinist's art is good steel, too much attention cannot be given to the selection of a steel of uniform quality. This can only be brought about through experience in working and using the different brands for purposes required, and when a grade has been procured which can be handled successfully and gives satisfaction in use, stick to it and never change until you are convinced that you have struck a better one.

After having selected the brands and grades of steel that are suited for the classes of work required, adopt some method of marking each separate brand so the workmen will be able to recognize them without the fire and water test. The best way to insure against difficulty arising from the mistakes in using the wrong brand of steel is to have each brand or grade striped with a different color paint. Have some one stripe the steels along their entire length, as soon as received, and either place each brand in a separate rack with the name of the steel on it, or have a board hanging near the steel rack with short stripes of paint of the colors used and the name of each brand next the stripe denoting it. In this manner the brand of steel desired can be found in a moment with the certainty that it will be the *right* brand.

Steel for Different Purposes.

For small reamers, taps, small round punches, which are to cut at slow speeds, and other tools of a like nature, use drill rod, not necessarily Stubs—any good American drill rod will answer as well. Never use a very high carbon steel for taps and dies or other threading tools.

Die Steel.

In no branch of the machinist's art should more attention be given to the importance of the proper selection of steel than in die-making, as the working qualities of the tools when finished and their efficiency depend upon this more than anything else.

When ordering steel which is to be used for dies be sure to specify that annealed steel is wanted, as the saving of time and labor in the working of it, and the certainty of the results in the hardening and tempering of it after the re-annealing, will be a source of gratification to the mechanic. When these results are considered the slight extra cost of annealed steel is insignificant.

As to the grade of steel to use for dies, be sure to get a good grade, and as there are several brands of steel on the market which are used principally for dies and punches no difficulty should be experienced in procuring a grade or brand which will prove suitable for any special class of sheet-metal work.

Steel Die Forgings.

When steel forgings are required, from which dies are to be made, the job should be given to a smith who understands this branch of his art, as in order for the forgings to machine well and allow of being hardened and tempered as desired, so that the finished tools will accomplish the required results, the smith must understand such work. As too high a welding heat, a raw weld joint, rapid cooling of the forging and other effects of carelessness are often responsible for the spoiling of an expensive tool in hardening, a good smith is necessary for such work.

The Treatment of High-Carbon Steel.

The treatment of high-grade tool steel is a subject which has been discussed often and to great length, but it is one of the greatest importance to steel users and too much cannot be written on it. How often has a piece of steel been condemned as being of inferior quality when the fault lay, not in the steel, but in those who had selected and used it. The causes of failure in using a high-grade steel are numerous. Often the proportion of carbon is not right for the purpose required; then again, the steel is overheated when forging, annealing, hardening or tempering, most frequently in the tempering process, which in high-grade steel is a delicate operation requiring knowledge, skill and experience.

It is impossible for a machinist to determine the correct hardening process for high-carbon steels unless he is familiar with the characteristic appearance of fractures of a specimen which has been treated properly. Any operator who has worked steel of good quality and is familiar with the appearance of the different fractures has no difficulty in avoiding injurious treatment during the hardening process. It is, however, impossible to describe the appearance of fractures of high-grade steel of various hardness in a manner to allow of their being understood by mechanics in general, or in fact to be practically useful to any great extent, this knowledge only being communicated to the operator through experience.

Experimental Treatment.

Some idea may be gained of the great and varied alterations produced in high-carbon steel through the different methods of hardening by a description of a test experiment. If a forged or rolled bar of high-grade steel is nicked at a number of places equidistant apart along its entire length a suitable specimen will be obtained for experimental purposes. Place one end of the bar in the fire far enough to allow of heating the first section up to the nick to a white heat. Thus the rest of the bar, being out of the fire, will be heated to a decreasing temperature toward the other end. As soon as the first section is at a white heat, thus burning the steel, through its being of a high carbon percentage, and the heat of the remainder of the bar becomes a dull red, take the bar from the fire and quench it instantly into a cold water bath. Leave the metal in the bath until cold and then remove and dry it. By testing with a file the first section will, of course, prove

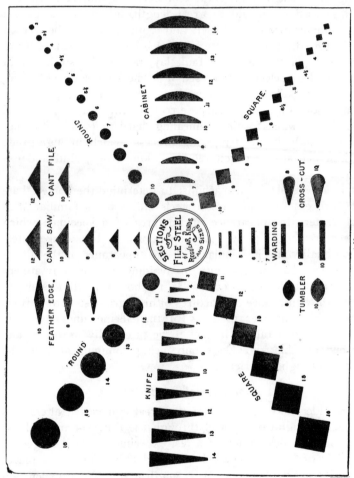

FIG. I.—SECTIONS OF FILE STEEL, SHOWING REGULAR SHAPES AND SIZES.

the hardest, and the intermediate sections of degrees of hardness passing from the softest to the hardest. Thus the conditions of the different sections, when broken apart at the fracture points, will show the operator the results in the steel when hardened at a given temperature. On breaking the pieces at each neck it will be noticed that very considerable changes have taken place in the grain of the metal. The first piece, which has been burnt, through heating to a white, has a very open and crystallized fracture, while the succeeding pieces are of a closer grain as they approach

FIG. 2.—SECTIONS OF FILE STEEL, SHOWING REGULAR SHAPES AND SIZES.

the end. Thus the selected piece or section, which has been subjected to the proper degree of heat in accordance with the carbon percentage of the steel, will be found to possess that perfectly even grain and velvety appearance which is looked upon by all experienced tool steel users as a condition to be prized in hardened steel. The first pieces will probably show cracks from being quenched at too high a temperature, while those at the other end will be hardened throughout as desired. Thus, through an experiment of this kind, we learn that in order to make a piece of steel hard and tough the temperature must be sufficiently high to allow of hardening it through, but not high enough to open the grain.

The Treatment and Working of Well-Known Brands of Tool Steel.

The brands of tool steel in general use throughout the United States and the ones which are best known and understood among steel users are Jessop's, Hobson's, Crescent, Styrain, Howe-Brown, Sanderson's, Capital and a number of self-hardening brands. In the following we give descriptions for the working of the different brands of which we have been able to obtain data. For all high-grade steels the directions will prove satisfactory. Figs. 1 and 2 show sections of shapes and sizes of file steel.

Heating for Forging.

For Jessop's steels heating for forging is, in its way, quite as important as heating for hardening; care and uniformity in the application of the heat in the first instance is very essential. Should the steel be overheated in this process no amount of care afterward will restore the steel to its former state or remedy the evil; therefore, when forging, watch the blast and see that the thin edges or exposed parts do not heat too fast.

In tools carrying a cutting edge, finishing cold and hammering hard is beneficial, such as forgings for cutting dies, for instance.

Heating for Hardening.

Then comes the vital process of hardening, and no fixed general rules will answer, as skill and experience are the only reliable standbys. However, a few points will help in the attainment of satisfactory results. Heat slowly and evenly in a charcoal or a coal fire or in a gas muffle. Most mistakes and accidents are due to the steel not being heated to the same temperature throughout; particularly is this so in large articles such as dies.

If possible, dip on a rising heat, that is, do not take a tool from the fire and wait until it becomes air cool; see that you get it the

FIG. 3.—LARGE SPIRAL FLUTED "HOB" TAP.

required heat and dip at once, always remembering that the lowest heat at which steel will harden satisfactorily gives the best results in hardness and toughness, conditions which must go together to insure satisfaction; therefore do not exceed a low red in heating.

Plain water, if clear and cold, will generally allow of hardening sufficiently; if not, brine should be used. There are also a number of chemical compounds, receipts for which are given in another chapter of this book, which give excellent results; a practical experiment is, however, the safest to go by in adopting them for hardening tools for different uses.

To harden small, intricate and thin tools, which must not twist or warp excessively during the process, an oil bath will be found the best to quench in.

Do not expose heated steel to a current of air, especially in winter, and in intricate dies or milling cutters it is safer to allow them to cool thoroughly before removing them from the quenching solution. In quenching, a strong jet of water will help to attain good results when hardening large dies, etc.

If you think that a little soap or oil has got into your water bath, a handful of lime will clean it. The best way to do in a case of this kind is to simply empty the tank and refill it with perfectly clear water.

In hardening milling cutters or similar tools, in which there is likely to be a great strain placed upon the tooth at its exposed edges, it is best to take the chill out of the water by plunging a red hot piece of cast iron into it. In some cases it is necessary to protect exposed portions of such tools with clay and thus lessen unequal contraction and strain.

Never attempt to harden tool steel without having first removed the outer scale or skin; this applies especially to annealed steel. Also always remember that overheated steel will usually crack when plunged into cold water. At all events it will be useless unless restored.

Treatment of Jessop's High-Speed, Self-Hardening Steel.

Heat the steel uniformly and with moderate care, forge to shape at bright red and do not hammer cold. Having forged to shape, the best results in hardening may be obtained by allowing the tool to cool before the process.

To harden: Heat the nose of the tool to almost a white heat;

do not be afraid of burning it, but when white hot remove and allow to cool away from the hearth. From the high temperature a thick scale will result, which should be thoroughly removed by grinding on a wet stone. A dry emery stone is usually more or less detrimental to any steel.

After using a tool made from this steel for some time, and regrinding five or six times to keep up its cutting qualities to the fullest extent, it is found advisable to re-harden as described above, doing this without re-dressing the tool unless the shape requires alteration.

Annealed Tool and Die Steel.

Every mechanic appreciates the advantages to be gained in using annealed tool and die steel, as it obviates the necessity of annealing before roughing, economizes time and overcomes all risks of overheating or burning during the process of annealing. After roughing it may be heated to a low heat and left to cool and then finished, when the results in hardening and tempering will give perfect satisfaction.

Treatment of Annealed Tool and Die Steel.

In hardening tools made from ready annealed steel, heat slowly and uniformly to a low red and use as little blast as possible. This is especially needful in large die steel.

In forging, above all things avoid overheating and a strong blast. Apply the heat uniformly, turning over the article in the fire so as to give the heat a chance to reach the center. Have the fire of sufficient size to allow of heating the article all over and see that it is free from sulphur or other impurities. Never try to heat a large block of steel in a small fire.

Treatment of "Capital" High-Grade Steel.

In working "Capital" steel it must be heated slowly and forged to shape at a heat suitable for ordinary cast steel. It must be heated gradually to a white welding heat and cannot be spoiled by overheating if it is removed from the fire on the first indication of its reaching a melting point. It must be placed instantly into a cold-air blast produced by a blower or compressed air. If the nose is to be used the tool should be held on a direct line with the blast, but not too close; as soon as the steel stops sparking turn on the full blast of air-pressure and hold the steel within about two inches of the nozzle until quite cold.

After the air-hardening process the tool must be thoroughly ground, as the high heat forms a thick scale which must be re-moved entirely in order for the tool to stand.

In hardening it is also advisable to have the cold air blast as

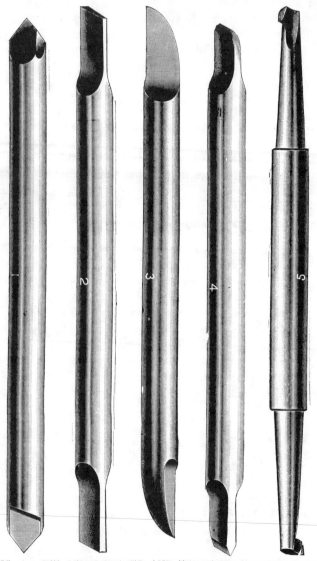

FIG. 4.—SET OF HARDENED AND TEMPERED TURNING TOOLS
FOR PRECISION LATHE.

near as possible to the heating arrangement, so that the tool can be transferred immediately from the fire to the blast. On no account let the point of the tool shift from the direct air current until the tool is cold. If the article is laid down while hardening it must be fastened securely so that the air blast will not shift it.

The Best Steel for Tools.

The question that has been asked more often than any other of steel experts, by men responsible for results in metal working, is: "What make of steel is the best for general tool work?" This question has never been answered satisfactorily and it never will, as no two men handle and work a piece of steel alike, and until mechanics follow instructions given for the working of the different brands they must find out through experience the best make of steel for their special purposes. Any of the leading brands of high-grade steel will prove satisfactory for general tool work if heated perfectly, and in these two last words lies the attainment of good results.

In order for the mechanic to work steel properly he must know the different brands and adopt them for purposes which experience has taught him they are the best suited. Get the general knowledge of the nature and peculiarities of the different brands of steel and decide for yourself the purposes for which they are best suited. When you obtain a brand that works well when used generally *stick* to it.

Testing Tool Steel.

When a number of tools are to be made from the same bar of steel, unless a piece of this particular bar has been used before and given satisfaction, it is well to test it, especially when expensive tools are to be made from it. A good way to do this is to cut off a thin disk from one end and harden it at a low red heat. After the piece has cooled, dry it and crack it through the center. Thus any defect which may run through the center of the bar will become apparent. If there are any defects, return the bar to the manufacturer.

The Grain of Steel.

If the steel proves sound the grain should be examined. In doing this do not wet the fracture, as this would discolor the steel and prevent examination. If the steel is good the grain will appear fine and close; if bad, a coarse appearance will be presented, similar to broken cast iron. A coarse grain steel should never be used for tools which will be subjected to much strain, such as milling cutters, for instance. For hardness, test the center of the fracture with a sharp, smooth file. If great hardness is required, break a piece so as to leave a sharp point; if the point cuts glass, the steel will harden satisfactorily throughout.

Testing Steel for Toughness.

A great many steels will show a fine grain and will be of sufficiently high carbon percentage to allow of hardening satisfactorily, but will not prove tough enough for general usage. In making expensive tools this quality should be determined before proceeding with the machining. Harden a disk and place it upon an anvil and strike the center a heavy blow with a hammer. If it breaks instantly it is too brittle and is not tough enough, but if, on the contrary, several blows are required to break it and at the last blow the disk flattens a bit, it is fine steel and may be used without fear of subsequent failure in hardening.

Economy in Testing Steel Before Using.

While these testing methods are rather costly in the beginning, and in a great many cases can be dispensed with, their adoption when making a number of costly tools will often prevent expensive mistakes. Where a large amount of tool steel is used, some one should be assigned to the task, and when a lot of steel comes in he should cut a disk off each bar in the power hack saw, mark each disk and its bar, and after a sufficient number of disks are at hand he should test them. Thus at a moderate cost the certainty of the steel being satisfactory for required uses will be determined, a large number of costly accidents possibly averted, and a vast amount of time saved through the obviation of individual testing by the tool-makers.

Decarbonized Steel Surfaces.

A fact which few tool-makers seem to realize, and one which if generally known would save much trouble, is that the surfaces of all steels as they come from the manufacturer are decarbonized and, of course, will not harden. This condition cannot be overcome in the present manufacture of steel, as the action of the oxygen in the air affects the steel in such a manner, as it is put through the various operations required in its production, as to burn out the carbon in the surfaces. For this reason do not select a piece of steel which will just "skin" up, but take a piece large enough to require taking a good-sized cut off before reaching the finishing surface.

How to Know Tool Steel from Mild Steel.

In a great many shops very little attention is given to the steel corner, rack, or box; the floor is the most popular place for steel storage in a number of shops. Very often machinery steels and tool steels are piled together in one heap, and when the machinist goes to secure a piece he has to wonder "which is which." There are any number of means for finding this out, but we give here a very quick way. To test a piece of steel, touch the end lightly against a dry emery wheel and watch the sparks as they strike. A tool steel gives forth a spark which seems to burst into a bright point of light when it strikes against the frame of the grinder, while a spark from machinery steel is merely a dull red incandescent particle. All air-hardening steels give forth bright red sparks.

Tool Holder and Tools.

The engraving, Fig. 5, shows a simple home made tool holder for lathe or planer, while Fig. 6 shows a set of tools to be used

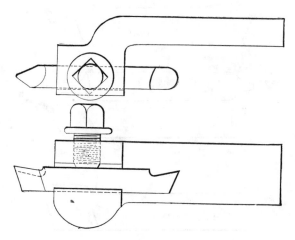

FIG. 5.—A LATHE TOOL HOLDER.

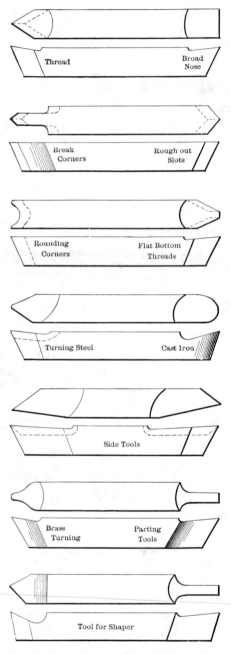

FIG. 6.—SET OF SELF-HARDENING STEEL-CUTTING TOOLS.

with it. Neither will require a description. A set of these tools and a holder of the construction shown will be found handy things for a tool-maker to have in his drawer.

Self-Hardening Steel Cutting Tools.

A great many machinists complain about self-hardening steel cutting tools, and say that it is impossible to accomplish fine results in turning or planed work with them, and for that reason a great many will not use them. Now, when they say that for fine work they are useless, they are right, as it is impossible to get the edges of such tools to keep a keen edge for any length of time so as to allow of taking smooth finishing cuts. But for medium cuts and feeds and coarse thread cutting, machining cast iron in the shaper, planer or lathe, for turning brass castings and also for accomplishing different operations on cast iron parts in the turret lathe, they are unequaled and should always be used where the production of machine parts at the minimum of cost and labor is imperative. For the face-milling of large castings, where inserted tooth cutters are adaptable, the self-hardening steel tools will be found to give the best results. There are several brands of self-hardening steel on the market in any one of which it will be found possible to hold an edge sufficiently keen to allow of its being used for the purposes herein enumerated.

Speeds of Cutting Tools.

To secure the best results from steel used for cutting purposes attention must be given to the use of calculations in or for determining the proper speed for the work or tool, according to conditions. As a rule the average machinist does not in ordinary practice make use of these rules, but instead depends on the knowledge acquired through experience and observation. For the benefit of those who are not familiar with rules for finding cutting speeds, and to obviate the necessity of guessing at the proper speed, we give approximate cutting speed at which tools or work should be run in the machining of different metals. Figs. 7 to 24 illustrate tool holders and tools and the manner in which they should be used.

Cutting speed for cast iron, 14 to 16 circumference or longitudinal feet per minute.

Cutting speed for malleable iron, 16 to 20 circumference or longitudinal feet per minute.

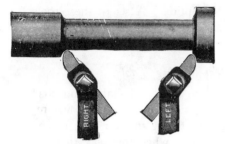

FIG. 7 —RIGHT AND LEFT SIDE
TOOLS, TURNING.

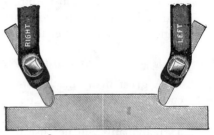

FIG. 8.—RIGHT AND LEFT SIDE
TOOLS, PLANING.

FIG. 9.—PLANER TOOL.

FIG. 10.—MANNER IN WHICH PLANER
TOOL IS USED.

FIG. 11.—KEYSEATING.

FIG. 12.—CUTTING-OFF TOOL.

FIG. 13.—OFFSET CUTTING-OFF TOOL.

FIG. 14.—TURNING TOOL FOR LATHE.

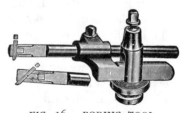

FIG. 16.—BORING TOOL.

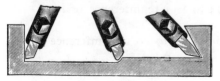

FIG. 15.—SHAPER TOOL.

FIG. 17.—BORING TOOL.

FIG. 18.—BORING.

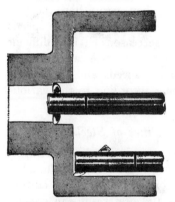

FIG. 19.—BORING TOOL.

FIG. 20.—CUTTING INSIDE THREAD.

FIG. 21.—THREAD TOOL.

FIG. 22.—"HOGGING" TOOL.

FIG. 23.—PARTS OF "HOGGING" TOOL.

FIG. 24.—"HOGGING" CUT.

Cutting speed for steel, 12 to 15 circumference or longitudinal feet per minute.

Cutting speed for brass, 28 to 40 circumference or longitudinal feet per minute.

The circumstances and conditions upon which slight variations of the speeds given above depend are numerous, among which are: Whether a roughing or finishing, coarse or fine cut is being taken; the form and shape of the cutting tools; the toughness and density of the metals worked upon, and the surface feet machined without regrinding the tool. There is a great deal of work done in the lathe or in the planer which requires tools which project far out of their holders. For such work the cutting speeds must be considerably less than here given. Then, very often, the texture of the metal is tough and hard, necessitating slower speeds and fine feeds in machining. For these reasons, it is a difficult matter to lay down any exact rules for the accurate calculating of cutting speeds; so we give approximate speeds and leave their variation to the machinist to determine according to the various conditions.

Cutting and Durability Qualities of Steel.

The capacity of steel to cut lies principally in its temper, while the durability of the cutting edges depends upon its quality and adaptability to the kind of work for the machining or cutting of which it is used. Thus to secure the best results in cutting tools, steel of the best quality must be used. The cost of good steel for tools should not be considered of much importance as compared with its efficiency, because the cost is insignificant when compared with the results possible to attain by its use. Take, for instance, a large milling cutter, or gang of small milling cutters, made from good steel and weighing a few pounds, will machine many tons of metal without requiring grinding if subjected to the proper hardening and tempering processes. The time required to machine a given surface depends very much upon the quality of the steel of which this tool or tools is or are made, and will vary thirty or forty per cent from a very slight difference in quality.

With a steel of a given quality the efficiency of the tools made from it depends most upon the knowledge and skill employed in the forging, annealing, hardening and tempering, and also upon the shape of the cutting edges. So in considering the different qualities of work performed by tools made from the same grade or brand of steel, we must first know of the amount of skill employed in the performance of the heating operations.

Judgment, Experience and Perception in the Working of Steel.

To a great many mechanics any steel which will harden is considered good steel. To harden, however, is a very simple matter, but to harden when heated to a definite degree requires skill, and to harden a piece of steel so that it will possess a definite degree of elasticity when tempered to a particular point of temperature after hardening requires skill and knowledge both. Thus if all steel which will harden is *good* steel, and as there is an absence of uniformity in the grades of steel in general use, the operator must rely on judgment, experience and perception to attain satisfactory results.

Even when the steel operated upon is of a uniform grade, the heating processes will not always bring forth uniform results, because steel decarbonizes somewhat by being heated, and thus a small piece or tool deteriorates by being heated in the open fire, and one often heated to repair or sharpen suffers in proportion. From all this it will be understood that hardening and tempering processes of steel must differ according to the size and nature of the work, the amount of uniformity required, and the results which the tools are required to accomplish. From all these considerations we are forced to conclude that the information of value to practical men and the only way to instruct them in the art of steel treatment is by presenting the practice of the best shops and tool-makers and giving the processes and conditions in connection with each other.

The First Effects of Heat.

Norton, in his "Elements of Natural Philosophy," says:

"The first effect of heat on any body, solid, liquid or aeriform, is to expand it.

"The expansion of gases may be readily shown by an air thermometer. This consists simply of a bulb of glass, with a long narrow stem, dipping into colored water. If the bulb be warmed by the hand, the air within will so expand that a portion will be expelled and rise in bubbles through the liquid. On cooling, the portion of air remaining will contract to its former volume, and the water will take the place of the air expelled.

"The experiment may then be continued indefinitely. The expansion and contraction may be measured by the scale attached to the stem; it will be found that all expand equally and regularly for successive increments of heat.

Unequal Expansion.

"The unequal expansion of different metals is well shown by a compound bar, made by riveting together two bars of iron and brass, at different points along their whole length. . . .

"If the bar is straight at ordinary temperature, it will so bend when hot water is poured on it that the brass will be on the convex side of the curve, and bend in the opposite direction when cold water is poured on it. The brass expands and contracts more than the iron, and the bar curves to accommodate the inequality of the length which results. This principle has been applied to the construction of metallic thermometers.

Heat Effects on Clay.

"Clay does not expand by heat, but contracts permanently, by reason of chemical changes in its particles. In the experiments detailed, the bodies will be found to contract on cooling and assume their original volume as soon as they attain their former temperature. Certain metals, as lead and zinc, are exceptions to this law of cooling, the contraction being at each time a little less than the expansion.

"From this experiment it is evident (1) that the volume of all bodies is increased by heat; (2) that this increased volume is due to motion among the molecules of the bodies, which tends continually to separate them; (3) that the intensity of the heat may be measured by the degree of the molecular motion. From these and other considerations it is assumed that *heat is that mode of molecular motion which may be measured by the expansion of bodies.*

"By this definition it is understood, (1) that the molecules of every body are in continual motion; (2) that when this motion increases in intensity the body becomes warmer; (3) that when this motion decreases in intensity the body becomes cooler. An older theory, which regarded heat as imponderable matter, has been generally discarded, while some of its terms have been retained; hence it must be understood that when heat is described as passing from one body to another, it means that the molecular motion of one body is communicated to the molecules of another, and not that any material agent has passed between them.

The Amount of Force Exerted in Expansion or Contraction.

"The amount of force exerted in expansion and contraction is enormous, for it is equal to that which would be required to stretch or compress the material to the same extent by mechanical means.

"Water, at the temperature 128 deg. Fahrenheit is compressed .000044 of its volume by the pressure of one atmosphere. On being heated from 32 deg. Fahrenheit to 212 deg. Fahrenheit it expands .0466 of its volume. Therefore, to restore boiling water to its bulk at freezing would require a pressure of over one thousand atmospheres. The expansive force of water for each degree Fahrenheit is nearly ninety pounds per square inch. Hence, if a closed vessel be completely filled with cold water, it must speedily burst when heat is applied.

"A bar of wrought iron expands, for each degree Fahrenheit, with a force of nearly two hundred pounds to the square inch. This force had a curious application in the Museum of Arts and Trades in Paris. The walls of an arched gallery had bulged outward by the weight of the arch. Iron bars were placed across the building and screwed into plates on the outside. The alternate bars were then heated, and as soon as they had expanded the plates were screwed up tightly to the walls. As the bars cooled and contracted, they drew the walls closer together. The operation was repeated until the walls had attained the vertical position.

"On the same principle tires are fastened on wheels. The tire, made a little smaller than the wheel, is heated red hot, and while expanded is placed in position. On cooling, it not only secures itself on the rim, but holds all the other parts of the wheel in position.

"It is often necessary to take into account the changes of length produced by heat. In railways a small interval must be left between the ends of the iron rails. Iron bars built into necessary lengths should be left free at one end.

"Brittle substances, as glass and cast iron, often crack on being heated suddenly, because the outside is heated sooner than the inside, and thereby causes an unequal expansion. A sudden cooling, by inducing unequal contraction, has the same effect. The thicker the plate the greater the liability to fracture.

The Second Effect of Heat.

"The second effect of heat on a solid is to change its molecular condition to melt it. Some solids, as paper, wood and wool, do not melt, but are decomposed. The temperature at which solids melt differs for different substances, but is invariable for the same substance, if the pressure is constant. This temperature is called the melting point.

Table of Expansion from 32 deg. F. to 212 deg. F.

	Linear.	Cubical.
Solids.	1	1
Flint glass	1/1248	1/416
Platinum	1/1131	1/377
Steel	1/926	1/309
Iron	1/846	1/282
Brass	1/536	1/179
Silver	1/524	1/175
Zinc	1/340	1/113
Tin	1/516	1/172
Fluids.		
Mercury		1/55
Water		1/21.3
The fixed oils		1/12.5
Alcohol		1/9
Air and permanent gases		180/491"

Kinds of Steel Produced in America by the Crucible and Open Hearth Processes.

Steel is produced in America by the crucible and open-hearth processes in bars, rods, sheets, plates, wire, forgings and rolled shapes.

The different kinds of steel produced by these methods comprise: Fine tool and die steel, self-hardening steel, ax and hatchet steel, cutlery steel, surgical and fine knife steel, composite die steel, oil well and artesian bit steel, mining drill steel, annealed die-blocks and cutter blanks, tool steel forgings, circular and long saw plates, boiler and fire box plates, hot-rolled and cold-rolled strip steel, polished high-grade drill rods and wire, needle wire, resistance wire rods, music wire rods, nickel steel rods; wire of every grade, shape and size, bright, annealed and tempered; crucible steel rods, clock and watch spring steel, pen steel, magnet steel, heavy gun forgings and projectiles, gun barrel steel, spring steel, machinery steel, merchant bar steel, machinery steel forgings, cold-drawn screw steel, hammer and sledge steel, welding steel, soft center and soft back plow steel, agricultural steel of all descriptions, sleigh shoe and toe-calk steel, wedge steel, laminated safe steel, skate steel, etc.

One of the largest producers of steel in the world, by the crucible and open-hearth processes, is the Crucible Steel Company, of America, Pittsburg, Penn. This company's products include all of the steels above enumerated as well as many others too numerous to mention.

CHAPTER II.

The Terms Defined.

Annealing, hardening and tempering, are three terms used to distinguish the different processes through which tool steel and various other metals are required to pass in order to allow of their being used for the various purposes required in the arts. In order that the mechanic may be able to adopt these processes to the best advantage in the making of tools for different kinds of work, he must learn that annealing means something more than heating a piece of steel red hot and allowing it to cool; hardening more than heating red hot and plunging into water, and, that tempering, something more than coloring a piece of steel. In fact he must realize that the annealing, hardening and tempering of steel is an art in itself, and that in order to become skilled in it, constant vigilance, experience and study are necessary, from "the ground up."

Metals are annealed by slowly cooling them from a high temperature. Annealing generally increases the flexibility, softness, and ductility of bodies, and in this manner metals that have become brittle through excess of strain in rolling, drawing, twisting, hammering, forging or other mechanical means, may have their properties restored by annealing.

Steel and a number of other metals, if cooled suddenly after having been heated to a high temperature, become more brittle and more elastic than before. For instance, if a piece of tool steel is heated to a white heat and then plunged into a bath of ice-water or mercury, it will become almost as hard as a diamond, and will be very elastic and so brittle that it can only be used for drilling tempered steel or chilled iron, or for coining and engraving dies and files of the hardest kinds.

When steel is in its softened condition it may be worked into any shape required in the arts. To harden steel after it has been worked, it is strongly heated and suddenly cooled, and as it is rendered too brittle by this hardening process (for ordinary purposes, at least), something of its elasticity must be sacrificed and a portion of its hardness removed by reheating the steel to a lower temperature and allowing it to cool slowly. This process is called "drawing" or "tempering." The temper to which a piece of steel should be drawn depends upon the use to which it is to be put, and is regulated by varying the temperature of the second heating, the higher the degree of heat the softer the steel.

When a steel tool or article has been hardened, then polished or ground and reheated, the film of oxide on its surface becomes, at a temperature of 420 deg. F., of a light straw color, then through intermediate hues to a violet yellow at 509 deg. F., blue at 550 deg. F., while at 725 deg. F. the steel passes to a red heat. These colors guide the workman in his efforts to temper the tools as required. Light yellow is the temper required for all articles or tools requiring a keen edge; a deeper yellow for fine cutlery, while violet is the temper for table knives requiring flexibility more than a hard brittle edge, and blue for all articles or tools which are required to be very flexible.

How to Thoroughly Anneal High-Carbon Tool Steel Parts.

Very often a large number of accurate small tools are to be made from high-carbon steel, and as they are required to be hardened perfectly so as to not warp, bulge, crack or shrink excessively, they must be perfectly annealed before finishing.

The most satisfactory method for annealing high grade tool steel parts is to pack in granulated charcoal in an iron box, arranging the parts so that they will not come higher than within one inch of the top of the box, and cover with well packed charcoal. Then place the box in the furnace or forge and heat to a bright red, at which it should be held for some time, depending upon the size of the parts to be annealed. For instance, parts not over one inch in diameter or thick, if kept at a red heat for an hour, after a through heat, will be found to have annealed as desired; large pieces must be kept hot for a period corresponding to their size and shape. After the heat, allow the box to cool off slowly and do not remove the parts until perfectly cool.

The Proper Heat for Annealing.

It has been found through experience that the proper heat for annealing is almost a forging heat. Keep at a bright red long enough to overcome all strains which may have a tendency to manifest themselves during the hardening process. It is not well to use cast iron chips or turnings for packing, as they will decarbonize the steel to such an extent as to prevent successful hardening afterward. Packing parts too near to the walls of the annealing box will have almost the same effect as the chips; in fact, it will be worse, as the decarbonizing effect will be unequal and the surfaces nearest the box sides will be affected, thus making whatever hardening possible unequal.

Annealing in the Charcoal Fire.

A great many shops have not the facilities to allow of using the above described annealing process, and in such very satisfactory results may be attained by heating the steel in a good charcoal fire to about an even forging heat. After heating, put a few inches of the fire ash in a box, and on top of the ash place a soft pine board, then place the heated work on top and cover the box. The wood will char and smolder and the steel will remain hot for a considerable period. Often a box of cold ashes may be used to accomplish the same results to a less extent, as the cold ashes or lime—either. one acts the same—are apt to chill the hot steel. However, when either of the three materials are used hot, good results will be obtained.

Good Steel for Good Tools.

One of the points that a great many mechanics seem to forget is the necessity of having good steel in order to do good toolmaking. Often upon asking a toolmaker, who was engaged in making a tool or die, what brand of steel he was using, the writer has been met with the answer: "I don't know." Make it your business to discover the best brands for different purposes and then stick to them. A steel that is good steel will show, when hardened and broken, a white fracture free from coarse spots. Get a steel of a carbon percentage that will allow of its being annealed and hardened at a low red heat, as steel which requires a very high heat to anneal and harden, will, nine times out of ten, prove utterly unsatisfactory, and tools made from it will crack, chip or spring when in use.

Annealing.

Although it does not seem to be generally known, the successful hardening of a piece of steel depends greatly on the annealing of it previous to machining it, and in order to harden properly it is necessary that the correct processes of annealing should be understood. Always anneal any odd-shaped piece, or one with an irregular-shaped hole in it, after having roughed it down. The best way to anneal such pieces is to pack them in charcoal in an iron box, being sure to have as much charcoal at the sides of the box as at the bottom, in order that the heat shall not penetrate too quickly. The box should be kept at a red heat for an hour, and then left in the ashes over night to cool. The proper heat for such pieces in annealing should always be higher than the heat required to harden the same piece. Experience has taught us that a heat almost as high as a forging heat will be the means of overcoming any undue tension or strain which may become apparent when the piece is hardened.

An Annealing Box for Small Parts.

A good way to make an annealing box for small parts is to take a piece of, say, 3-inch iron pipe about 10 inches long. Tap both ends of the pipe and fit plugs to them; cast iron will do. One of the ends may then be closed and the charcoal and parts to be annealed packed in, after which the other plug can be screwed in. With a box of this kind no sealing is necessary, as the screw plugs prevent the entrance of the air.

Water Annealing.

Very often a piece of steel is required for a repair job or some other job in a hurry, and there is no time to anneal it in the regular way. At other times a piece which has been hardened requires to be machined. When confronted with the above conditions, a tool-maker can fall back on the "water annealing" and after he has tried it a few times he will be delighted with the results. There are several methods of doing this, and we give here the best of them all: The mechanic may adopt any of them, according to the results secured from each. The first method is to heat the steel slowly to a dull cherry red; then remove it from the fire and with a soft piece of wood try the heat, as it decreases, by touching the steel with the end of the stick. When the piece has cooled so that the wood ceases to char, plunge the steel quickly into an oil and water bath. On machining the steel it will be found to be very soft.

The second method for water annealing is to heat the steel

slowly to a red heat, then allow it to lie in the ashes a few minutes until almost black, then drop it into soapsuds and allow it
to cool.

Very often a piece of steel annealed in this manner will turn
out much softer than if annealed in the regular manner by packing
in powdered charcoal and allowing it to cool over night. A good
way to make sure as to the time to drop the steel into the bath,
is to allow it to cool until almost black, then touch it with a file,
if the steel does not brighten for an instant and then turn blue,
wait a few seconds and repeat the experiment. If, upon the
second trial, the blue appears and then a spark right afterward,
drop the steel instantly into the bath, and when cool it will be
found to be as "soft as butter."

Sometimes a piece of steel which is to be used as a punch or
die blank, upon starting to machine it, proves hard, although it
has been annealed. When this is the case, never try to finish it
before reannealing it; instead, rough it down, clean out the centers and anneal it over again. The time required to reanneal a
piece of steel will be more than made up in the machining of it.

The Effects of the Water Anneal.

Although it may seem strange to some, it is a fact that results
possible to attain in steel which has been water annealed cannot
be obtained by any other methods. Water annealing seems to
give a certain texture to the grain of the steel, which is not exactly softness, but is different from that obtained by charcoal ash
annealing. When a piece of steel has been properly water annealed
and is turned in the lathe using a lubricant, it will present a
strange dead-white appearance and the turnings will be short
and come off like little bristles.

In steel annealed in the usual manner the turnings will generally come off in long close-curled lengths, and the surface
of the work will present a more or less torn texture, even when
the tool used is very keen. This tearing is caused by the steel
being so soft as to give way and crowd up into little lumps just
slightly ahead of the cutting edges of the tool. Thus in cutting
screw threads in ordinary annealed steel it is almost impossible to
get a smooth, clean thread.

The water annealing, however, seems to overcome this un-
pleasant feature, in that it seems to give the requisite stiffness
of texture to prevent this tearing. Considering the results, the

water anneal will contribute to the best results being attained in a large variety of lathe work.

We are unable to state just what chemical or molecular action the water anneal has on steel. It is not a softening action, as compared with the effects of ordinary annealing, but instead a stiffness and tightness of the particles which allows the cutting edge of the tool to creep beneath the shell and peel it off.

The Annealing of Tap Steel.

Most of the large establishments in which taps, reamers, etc., are manufactured have most of their steel annealed at the places where it is made. This has been done for some years with the possible exception of the steel from which long stay-bolt taps are made, they having been found to require more care in annealing than the steel manufacturers give them.

During an interview a few years ago, Mr. F. A. Pratt, of the famous American firm of Pratt & Whitney, spoke as follows in regard to the working of tap steel:

"We have most of our tap steel annealed at the place where it is made. We have had it done in this way for some years, with the exception of our long stay-bolt taps, which we have found to require more care in annealing than the steelmakers give them.

"More steel is injured, and sometimes spoiled, by over-annealing than in any other way. Steel heated too hot in annealing will shrink badly when being hardened; besides, it takes the life out of it. It should never be heated above a low cherry red, and it should be a slower heat than it is when being hardened. It should be heated slowly and given a uniform heat all over and through the piece.

"This is difficult to do in long bars and in an ordinary furnace. The best way to heat a piece of steel, either for annealing or hardening, is in red hot, pure lead. By this method it is done uniformly and one can see the color all the time. We do some heating for annealing in this way, and simply cover up the piece in saw-dust, and let it cool there, and we get good results. All steelmakers know the injurious effects of over-heating steel and of over-annealing, but their customers are continually calling for softer steel and more thorough annealing. Until users are educated up to the idea of less annealing and to working harder steel, both will suffer, for the user will continually complain of poor steel.

"Several years since we caught on to the fact that steel was injured by over-annealing, and that good screw threads could not be cut in steel that was too soft; our men would rather take the steel bar direct from the rolls without any annealing than take the risk of annealing. At present we get it from the makers in passable condition, but not as it should be, and unless the steelmakers find some way to heat the bars to a uniform heat, and at a low cherry red, we must either use it raw from the bar or anneal it ourselves. We find, also, that this soft annealing makes a much greater shrinkage and spoils the lead of the thread, and that from the bar without any annealing there is very little trouble in this respect.

"When O. H. and Bessemer machine steel was first introduced it was poorly made and hard to work. Users constantly urged the makers to make it softer, until when a maker could say his steel was as soft as iron, and not more than 0.10 to 0.15 of 1 per cent. carbon, he had the market. This company found out early that this soft machine steel was almost worthless. A shaft would bend easily in working, and if a lead screw was to cut it was not possible to get a smooth thread and a good finish.

"Now we either make shafts and spindles of cast steel of a high carbon or of machine steel of about 50 per cent carbon, without annealing. Our men kicked at first, but now they complain if it is soft, because they cannot cut a good thread and cannot keep it as true."

Re-Annealing Tap Blanks.

Often, from improper annealing, a tap blank proves too hard for thread cutting, this coming about in the annealing processes, from not heating properly or not knowing the nature of the steel. When this is the case always re-anneal the blank, and the loss of temper and wearing out of good tools in trying to cut a thread on too hard stock will be obviated. Before re-annealing take a rough cut-off and clean out the centers.

How to Heat for Annealing.

When annealing steel, heat very slowly to a red—never heat it hot enough to raise scale—and allow lots of time for cooling. A piece of steel heated hot enough to scale will never work well unless re-annealed by some method which will restore it from its almost burnt state.

Annealing a Small Quantity of Steel.

When only a small quantity of steel is required heat to a cherry red in a charcoal fire and pack in sawdust in an iron box. Keep the steel in the pack until cold. For a large quantity, which is required to be very soft, pack with granulated charcoal in an iron box as follows: Having at least ½ or ¾ inch in depth of charcoal in the bottom of the box, add a layer of granulated charcoal to fill spaces between the steel, and also ½ or ¾ inch space between the side of the box and the steel, then more steel, and finally 1 inch in depth of charcoal well packed on top of the steel. Heat to a red and hold for from two to three hours and do not remove the steel from the box until cold.

Annealing Steel in the Open Fire.

Although the annealing of steel can be best accomplished by some of the regular packing materials, there are cases, such as an emergency job, when this cannot be resorted to, because of the time necessitated. When a piece of annealed steel is wanted in a hurry, try heating in an open fire and water annealing—heating in a charcoal fire to a dull red, then letting the steel cool naturally in the day light until the red disappears, and then quenching in cold water.

Quick Methods for Softening Steel.

In the following we give a few methods for the quick annealing of steel, gathered from various sources:

Cover over with tallow, heat to a cherry red in a charcoal fire and allow it to cool itself.

Heat the steel to a low cherry red and allow to cool in a dark place until black. Then quench in the juice or water of common beans.

Cover with clay, heat it to a cherry red in a charcoal fire and allow to cool slowly.

To Anneal Doubtful Steel.

There are some kinds of steel which will not anneal satisfactorily even when packed in air-tight boxes in powdered charcoal. To anneal steel of this kind, cover it with fine clay and heat to a red heat and allow to cool over night in the furnace.

Annealing Chilled Cast-Iron Dies for Drilling.

As drawing and forming dies are often made of chilled cast

iron, and as not infrequently holes are required to be drilled in them, it is well to know how to soften it to allow of drilling the holes. To do this, heat the die to a cherry red and let it lie on the coals. Then place a piece of brimstone, circular in shape and a little larger in diameter than the hole to be drilled, on the spot where the hole is to be. Let the die lie in the fire until it has died out and the metal has cooled, and the brimstone will have softened the iron entirely through within the radius of its diameter when solid.

Annealing White or Silver Iron.

To anneal white or silver iron so that it may be drilled or chipped, put it into a steel furnace or other converting furnace together with a suitable quantity of ironstone, iron ore, some of the metallic oxides, lime, or any other combination of these substances reduced to a powder, or any other substance capable of combining with or absorbing the carbon of the crude iron. The more or the longer the heat is applied, the more nearly malleable the iron will become.

The Annealing of Malleable Castings and the Manufacturing of Malleable Iron Machine Parts.

One of the largest establishments in this country devoted to the manufacture of malleable iron machine parts, is situated in Hoosick Falls, N. Y., and is controlled by the Walter A. Wood Mowing and Reaper Machine Company. A description of their plant, methods, etc., will tend to an intelligent understanding of how malleable iron machine parts are produced.

The Foundry and Preparation of the Castings.

The malleable department, exclusive of its sheds, has a floor space of over 163,000 square feet, the foundry alone measuring 485 x 125 feet. In this department, in which 350 men are employed, of whom 135 are molders, there are three furnaces with a capacity of three heats each in a twelve-hour day. The largest furnace, almost at the entrance of the foundry, will melt fourteen tons of metal at each heat, while the other two in the center of the foundry and at the extreme end, respectively, will each melt ten tons.

The castings produced are mostly of small size and are made from gated patterns. After they have been removed from the molds they are broken from the gates and are sent to the preparing department, where they are sorted, and all lumps, fins and gate joints are removed. The castings as they come from the molds are almost as brittle as glass and it is possible to split or break them with a light blow of a hammer. It is very interesting to watch the men in this operation. They can take a casting, set the edge or lump to be removed on an iron block and break it off at the joint with one blow, leaving the portion where the joint was as smooth as the rest of the casting.

Annealing Furnaces—Packing the Castings.

After the castings have been sorted and prepared they go to another department to be packed into the annealing pots. These pots are cast, and are about 24 inches long, 12 inches deep and 12 inches wide, and an inch thick. A mixture consisting of common sand, fine steel turnings and steel scale from the rolling mills is then wet with sal-ammoniac (which prevents the steel turnings and scale from adhering to the castings during the annealing process) and packed around the castings in the annealing pots. The pots are now taken to the annealing room. In this room there are eight ovens, the walls of which are three feet thick and the tops and bottoms four feet thick. To build each of these ovens 4,500 red brick and 1,500 white or firebrick were required. In each oven there are flues three feet square, running the full length of the oven and out into the stack at one end. There is also one intermediate flue, and a flue at each side into which the crude oil blast is fed.

Different Methods of Packing Castings in Pots.

There are various methods for packing castings for annealing. The term "packing" is a shop one applied to the class of materials which are used for the above purpose, and in addition, supply oxygen or have the latter in their composition. A number of different materials are used for the former purpose which are used principally on lighter castings. Almost anything that will stand up well while hot is suitable, like ground burned fire brick, iron borings, and sand. As they of themselves do not supply oxygen, it is necessary in using them that oxygen be obtained by means of a coating of rust or oxide upon the castings either before or after charging the pots. In rusting them before, much of the oxide becomes rubbed off in packing. Packing the castings wet will do, provided there is some certainty of their being oxidized before heating. Wetting the packing with diluted ammonia is a very sure means, and is the most satisfactory way of handling this material.

Packing or charging castings in the pots, so that they retain their shape and do not scale or warp while hot, is a process that cannot be well described. In general, they should be packed with a view to keeping the packing in close contact with the castings during the settling of the contents of the pot. For instance, flat plates or sections should be packed on edge; if on the side, they will scale on the bottom, from which the packings have settled. This explains why some castings scale and others do not in the same pot. Castings having projections or unequal sides, which can therefore be stacked on top of each other, are built up from the bottom plate with a view to balancing the pile. All long sections and long castings, unless packed in pots that will admit of their being placed horizontal, should be set upon the bottom plate vertically. I have seen castings 5 feet long become ¾ inch longer than the pattern, because they were packed some inches above the bottom plate and hung in the pot during settling. As a general rule, there is a relation between the amount of the packing and the castings, or between the oxygen in the packing and the carbon in the castings; there can therefore be a condition where there is not sufficient packing between the castings to anneal. There should always be an excess in favor of the packing. The packing of the castings is carried upward with a view to meeting the unequal heating of the pots—that is, heavy castings in the top and light ones in the bottom, separated by plates when the occasion requires it. Beginning with the bottom plate, the first pot is usually a new one. They do not take the heat readily, on account of the sand upon them, and, for this reason should be broken in on top. Owing to their weight, however, it is not practical to use them there. Building or packing continues upward, the pots being placed according to their age, the top pots passing through the service.

Annealing, Straightening and Finishing of Malleable Castings.

In the malleable department of the Wood works, in each annealing oven, pots containing twenty tons of castings are packed as close together as possible, after which the vents and doors are sealed up and the ovens are heated. It requires twenty-four hours of steady blast to get the ovens and castings to a white heat. They are then kept at that temperature for five days and five nights, after which the blasts are turned off and the vents at the tops of the ovens opened. After the vents have been open for five hours the door is pulled down and five hours later the nearest pots are removed, and in the course of a few hours the others are taken out and allowed to cool. They are then dumped and the castings are sorted. All that have cracked or blistered or have warped excessively are thrown out. The good castings are then sent to the straightening department to be straightened and reformed, so as to fit the jigs and fixtures which are used for machining those which are required to be machined and to make the others interchangeable. The straightening and re-forming of the castings are accomplished by dies in powerful presses. There are seven different machines, one a hydraulic press of seven tons, one five-ton power press, and two powerful drop hammers. On shelves surrounding the straightening room are hundreds of sets of dies. The dies for the large castings are of gray iron, while those for the small parts are of hard iron. The dies are cast in the department's own foundry by first getting a plaster model of the inside of the master patterns and one of the outside and then casting the dies from this model.

After the straightening and re-forming process, the castings are sent to the grinding and finishing department. Here all lumps and fins which were not removed before the annealing are ground off. The parts to be machined are finished in special jigs and fixtures on the drill press, milling machine or lathe, as most suitable, and the castings are then ready for the storeroom.

As every size and style of casting produced in the foundry is numbered, and as the numbers run from 1 to 2,503, some idea may be formed of the storage space required. The patterns used are of composition metal. They are stored in a fireproof vault, 65 by 25 feet and 12 feet high.

Heating the Annealing Ovens.

To heat the annealing ovens, crude petroleum is used, the oil being pumped from three tanks sunk in the ground 300 feet from the ovens and 200 feet from the engine-room in which pumps are located. One tank holds 13,000 gallons of oil and the other two 6,000 gallons each. The large tank is located beneath the railroad track and is filled from tank cars, and this in turn fills the small ones. The pump used to pump the oil to the annealing

ovens runs continually and has not been shut down twelve hours
in a year.   To melt the iron used in the malleable iron foundry
soft coal is used, the furnaces being so constructed as to allow
of the coal being placed in the front part and the metal and other
materials required to produce hard iron at the back, the heat
being driven in on the mixture by air pressure.

General Matter Relative to Malleable Iron Manufacturing.

Mr. Robert Leith, the superintendent of the department, has
been with the Wood Company for twenty-five years, and has been
responsible for the many innovations in his department tending
to economic production, one of which is to use in his foundry all
of the scrap steel produced in the main works.   He has used 100
pounds of the scrap steel to every ton of iron, and has secured the
very best of results by so doing.   Formerly it was necessary to
sell the scrap steel for almost nothing, in comparison with its
cost to the firm, but now the malleable department disposes of
all of it.   The output from the malleable department per week
is usually 150 tons of good castings, the bad work coming from
the foundry and annealing department not being counted.   The
power required for the department is derived from a 150 horse-
power engine, which has been in use over twenty-five years, and is
to-day a fine example of what care and a good engineer can do
for an engine in regard to its longevity.

On the harvesting machinery manufactured by the Wood
Company a great deal of chain is used.   The links composing
these chains are produced in the malleable department and the
chains are assembled and finished there.   The links are cast from
gated patterns, as many as fifty links to each mold.   The gating
is done in such a manner that when the castings have been
broken from the gate bars very little irregularity of surface is
evident; what projections remain are ground off after the annealing process.   The chains are assembled in continuous lengths by
an automatic machine, the links being fed through a chute at the
front and the chain fed out automatically at the back.   The
chains are subjected to various tests to insure their being the
length required.   Often (as the links are not machined before as-
sembling) some of the chains will be shorter than required, this
coming about through unequal rapping when molding, etc., the
part where the links unite being thicker in some than in others,
the accumulation in the course of a number of links making quite

a difference in the length of the chain. This defect is overcome by means of another machine, in which the chains are stretched until they are of the required length.

There is a metal pattern shop connected with the department in which all the patterns used in the foundry are finished. In this shop some of the finest metal pattern-work that I have ever seen is turned out, as is evidenced by the fact that out of a thousand castings of a certain shape only two were found to be "off" enough to prevent their being machined in the fixtures provided for them. Besides producing all the malleable castings which the works require, the department also does custom work, and it has the reputation of having done some of the finest work in the country.

CHAPTER III.

The Heating and Cooling of Steel.

There are any number of shops in which a great deal of unnecessary expense is incurred in the annealing, hardening and tempering of steel through improper heating and cooling during the processes; and while often inexperience is the cause of such expense, more often the crude and obsolete means employed for heating and cooling are to blame.

The fact is obvious to all that where expensive tools are made, proper facilities should be provided for the heating processes through which they are put. If there is any economy in providing fine machine tools and employing skilled mechanics to make fine small tools and utterly ignoring the requirements for the annealing and tempering of them, we fail to see it.

Now, while a plain ordinary forge is all right and will be found to be all that is necessary for the annealing and tempering of rough tools, it will not do for fine ones. When it is considered that an accurate cutting tool which has been annealed properly before finishing, and then carefully and accurately hardened and tempered afterward, will accomplish many times the amount of work that an imperfectly treated one will, the expense incurred in providing suitable heating facilities is insignificant, when the longevity of the tools treated is considered. In shops where a fair number of fine cutting tools are made and used, the cost of proper heating arrangements will be made up in a short time by the money saved through the use of properly hardened and tempered tools. Another thing: after having installed a suitable hardening plant, hire a mechanic to run it who understands the treatment of steel. With this combination, and a supply of good high-grade steel, there will be no dissatisfaction with the working qualities of the cutting tools; if there is, there will be no excuse for it; carelessness will be to blame.

FIG. 25.—TYPES OF EXPENSIVE MILLING CUTTERS.

The only way to heat steel properly and thoroughly is to not expose it to the action of air when hot, as the air will decarbonize the surfaces considerably. Thus, when steel is heated in a muffle furnace an even degree of heat is assured and all air is excluded.

Proper Equipment for Hardening and Tempering.

The proper equipment for annealing, hardening and tempering tools of different types can be decided by noting the various descriptions for obtaining the best results given in this and other chapters of the book. A number of types of furnaces, mufflers and other arrangements are shown in this chapter and their use and adaptation for different classes of work explained.

Points to be Remembered.

To heat and cool steel properly, remember the following: Never heat a piece of steel which is to be annealed above a bright red. Never heat a piece to be hardened above the lowest heat at which it will harden, and the larger the piece the more time required to heat it is required, which will have to be higher than a smaller piece of the same steel, because of the fact that a large piece takes longer to cool than a smaller piece, as when a large piece of steel is plunged into the bath a large volume of steam arises and blows the water away from it, thus necessitating more time in the cooling. Thus, when the tool or die is very large, a tank should be used to harden it in, into which a stream of cold water is kept constantly running, as otherwise the red hot steel will heat the water to such a degree that the steel will remain soft.

The Location of the Heating Furnace.

Although in a great many shops very little importance is attached to the proper placing and locating of the furnace which is to be used during the hardening processes, it will be found that if the location chosen is in a darkened corner where the sun's rays will not come near it, the best results will be attained. No matter what kind of hardening is to be done, the heating arrangements should never be located where there is too strong a light, or where the sun shines in at any time of the day. If the light is uniform it will not be difficult to attain uniform results, while, on the contrary, if the light is too bright, there is a chance of heating the steel too hot and, when it becomes darker, not hot enough. When a uniform light is maintained during the day the men become accustomed to it and no trouble is experienced in getting the best of results.

The Use of Gas Blast Furnaces and Heating Machines.

The use of gas blast furnaces and heating machines has now become so extensive as to have almost completely superseded the old methods, and the furnaces and machines are now used in securing the highest possible efficiency in the use of heat for mechanical purposes as well as in the processes of metallurgy and chemistry.

Gas blast furnaces are designed for the economical use of gas as fuel in forges, crucible furnaces, annealing, enameling, case-hardening ovens, assaying, cupeling and other muffle furnaces, japanning ovens, and drying and baking kilns, in all of which the heat is generated by a properly proportioned mixture of gas and air, injected under positive pressure, through burners especially adapted to each of the different kinds of gas in common use.

Heating machines may be called "modern machine tools," made for special heating processes, as they are combinations of gas furnaces and moving machinery for the automatic feeding and discharging of work which is to be annealed, hardened, tempered or forged in quantities.

The chief advantages derived from the use of gas as a fuel are the perfect adjustment of temperatures to suit exact requirements, which is impossible with either solid or liquid fuel; the ease with which any desired degree of heat can be obtained by simple adjustments of two valves, the uniformity of its distribution within given space, the partial or complete absence of oxidation, and, generally, the perfectly uniform condition under which any heating process can be performed irrespective of the quantities of work to be heated.

The gas consumption, cost of gas as compared with other fuel, while an important factor in determining the adoption of gas furnaces for the cruder operation of melting or forging, scarcely deserves consideration with reference to furnaces or heating machines for hardening, tempering or annealing large quantities of work, because no approximately equal amount of perfect work can be produced by the use of any other fuel than gas.

Gas Blast Forges—Their Use.

Gas blast forges heat the work quickly, uniformly, and with little or no scale. They are always ready for use and develop the required amount of heat in a few minutes. They are used in machine shops for tool dressing and forging; in the production of quantities of small forgings, such as cutlery, and for drop forgings generally.

While offering decided advantages, no single gas forge or furnace can replace the ordinary coal forge in everything, because to be thoroughly effective, as well as economical in gas consumption, the gas forge must be made for a definite range of work, and its heating space limited so as to conform to its size and shape, with only fair allowance for clearance space.

In order to determine the applicability of any of the various styles of gas forges now on the market, the dimensions of the entrance, height, width, depth, and length of the heating chamber must be considered, and a fair allowance made for clearance. When samples of work to be done are furnished to the manufacturers of such machines, together with a statement of the quantities to be heated in any given time, they will design special forges.

When gas blast forges are used in forging the overheating of the metal is entirely prevented, a non-oxidizing atmosphere reducing the scale to a minimum, thus supplying properly heated stock as fast as it can be handled.

For welding, special forges should always be designed for any particular kind of work, so that the blast will be confined closely to the joint to be made. In welding tires, the diameter, width and thickness will determine the shape of the entrance to the forge and conform to it.

Combination Gas Furnace for General Machine Shop Work.

In Fig. 26 we illustrate a combination gas furnace ready to operate.

This furnace combines on one base three most useful furnaces for general machine shop and tool work. It will heat quickly and uniformly any piece or pieces that will go into its various openings. The muffle can be heated to a good heat for hardening in from ten to twelve minutes and kept at the desired temperature indefinitely. The forge will heat a piece 1 inch round to a good hardening heat in one minute, starting with the furnace cold. The crucible full of lead can be heated to cherry red in about thirty-five minutes.

A furnace of this type occupies very little room; does not require to be connected to chimney; can be placed right in the tool room or anywhere it is most convenient; can be started instantly, and covers a range of uses that makes it practically indispensable. All sorts of small tools, such as dies, milling cutters,

FIG. 26.—COMBINATION GAS FURNACE.

reamers, punches, taps, drills, springs, cutlery, marking rolls, etc., can be heated in the muffle under the best possible conditions.

A section of this combination furnace, showing the muffle with walls cut away to illustrate arrangements of combustion chamber and muffle, is shown in Fig. 27.

The flame is projected from the double burners downward into the chamber encircling the muffle; the lining is of such shape that a rotary motion is imparted to the flame, causing same to distribute itself evenly all over the inclosed space; the products of combustion are drawn off by the two small openings at the top of the chamber. The muffle is heated rapidly and evenly throughout; the degree of heat is under perfect control; the work is absolutely secluded from the products of combustion, a feature of the greatest importance in heating dies, milling cutters and other expensive tools. Absolute uniformity can be maintained; overheating can be entirely avoided, difficult pieces can be hardened without danger of cracking by reason of an even heat throughout.

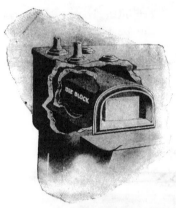

FIG. 27.—SECTION OF FURNACE CONTAINING MUFFLE, SIZE 5x8x15 INCHES.

Every manufacturer whose product involves the machining

FIG. 28.—FORGE SECTION OF FURNACE. SIZE OF OPENING, 3½x4½ INCHES. LENGTH, 14 INCHES.

of metals realizes the necessity of having modern apparatus for systematically applying heat, the output of his entire plant depending quite as much on the temper of his tools as on any other one condition. To get good results from tools use good steel and harden and temper it properly and the result will invariably be satisfactory.

The forge section of this furnace is shown in Fig. 28.

The combustion chamber is circular in form and is heated

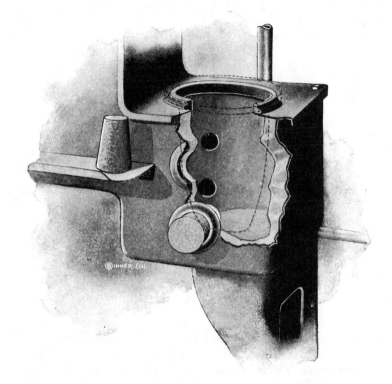

FIG. 29.—CRUCIBLE SECTION OF FURNACE.

by two burners which project the flame downward, the form of the lining giving the flame a rotary motion, evenly distributing it all over the chamber. The heat is under perfect control. This forge is very convenient for dressing and hardening tools and small forgings and for a variety of work where seclusion from the products of combustion is not required.

In Fig. 29 is shown the crucible section of the furnace. The

combustion chamber is circular in form; burners are so arranged
that the flame is projected into the chamber without striking the
crucible direct.   A rapid centrifugal motion is imparted, distributing the heat evenly and thoroughly.   The products of combustion are drawn off at vent in the rear.

For heating a great variety of small pieces the lead bath offers
many advantages over other methods.   By keeping the temperature of the lead at the proper point, overheating is impossible and
uniformity is secured.   Small pieces can be heated very rapidly
by this method.

For tempering a crucible (Fig. 30) similar to the one used for

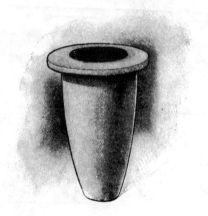

FIG. 30.—CRUCIBLE.

the lead bath is filled with beef tallow.   The exact heat required
to temper or draw the work is easily maintained as indicated by
a thermometer, which should be suspended in the bath.   For all
small tools, milling cutters, screw springs, punches, dies, etc., there
is no method of tempering (or drawing) so satisfactory as this.
Temperatures that have been found to give the best results can
repeatedly be employed.   The work to be tempered can be suspended in the liquid tallow by means of a wire basket, or other
convenient method, and can be left there indefinitely without danger of the temper running too low; all parts of the piece or pieces
immersed, whether of thin or thick section, will be evenly
heated.

Gas Forge for Small Work.

The gas forge shown in Fig. 31 is of a type commonly used for dressing and hardening tools and smaller forgings. The heating chamber is circular inside, and its capacity is limited in

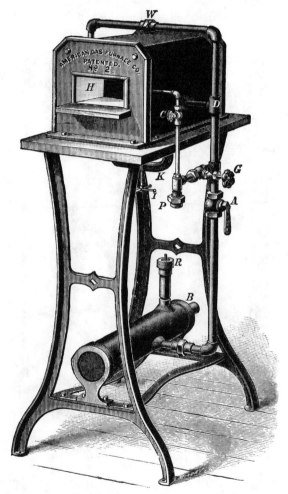

FIG. 31.—GAS FORGE. ENTRANCE, 6 INCHES WIDE BY 3 INCHES HIGH; DEPTH OF HEATING SPACE, 6 INCHES.

the size of the entrance to the heating chamber, and a corresponding opening in the back is ordinarily closed by a "plug," which can be removed when a clear passage through the furnace is required.   Two burners project into the heating chamber from the distributing pipe, D, W, so adjusted that direct contact of the flames with the work is avoided.   Perfect combustion is steadily maintained, the work is quickly and evenly heated and oxidization reduced to a minimum.

The furnace is connected with air by a tin pipe at B, and the

FIG. 32.—GAS FORGE FOR HEATING DROP FORGINGS.

cock A controls the air supply.   Gas connects with union from the nearest supply pipe by ¾-inch pipe at P, and globe valve G controls the gas supply.   The small cock C feeds a "pilot light" in the mouth of the furnace, which is left burning so as to instantly light the forge when the main supply is turned on.   The bottom of the furnace can be cleaned of scaling by removing a plug which is held in place by the set screw I, which passes through the hanger, K. The air relief valve R is a test valve to show the air pressure at the furnace, and when this has been found sufficient it can be weighted down tight.

Gas Forge for Heating Drop-Forgings.

The style of forge shown in Fig. 32 is extensively used for drop forgings, to heat blanks continuously and keep them at the proper heat. The heating space is 10 inches deep, 8 inches wide and 3 inches high. The burners, B, penetrate the chamber from opposite sides and the flames do not strike the work direct. The blanks rest upon a fire brick bottom, which is removable from the rear for cleaning out the chamber. This forge is extensively used in connection with oil gas, but can be adapted to every other kind.

Air Tempering Furnace.

Air tempering furnaces of the type shown in Fig. 33 are used for drawing the temper of steel work of all kinds, but more especially for small·light work in quantities. While cutters, punches, dies and knife blades are perfectly tempered in heated oil, in oil tempering furnaces, the air tempering furnace is used when the oil stain is objectionable, or when it is desired to show a bright, clear, temper color of any desired shade, from a light straw to a blue or gray.

The furnace contains an iron muffle with a horizontal partition in the bottom which forms an air-heating chamber below the level of the entrance into which the air is forced from the blower which operates the furnace, the injection of which is controlled by the valve H. From this air heating chamber the heated air is distributed through numerous fine holes so as to keep the muffle filled with heated air under a slight pressure, which is exerted around a thermometer stem when the door is closed.

The burner is controlled by the air valve A, and the gas valve, G. The connection with blower is to the drum, D, and gas is brought to the gas valve, G. The burner distributes the heat evenly under the muffle and around it, so that the atmospheric temperature within the working space of the muffle is perfectly even throughout.

The work is placed upon a wire tray and evenly distributed over its surface, and is constantly subjected to the action of fresh air heated to the proper degree.

The tray containing the work rests upon the open grating

shown in the cut, which is raised above the bottom of the muffle, and the heated air is forced through and around the work from the perforated heating chamber, thus coming in contact with freshly heated air constantly.

The operation is as follows:

It will require about 40 minutes to heat a furnace of this type

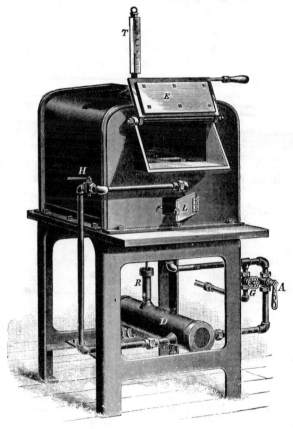

FIG. 33.—AIR TEMPERING OVEN.

to the 600 deg. required for a blue temper. This temperature being indicated by the thermometer, the work is inserted and the door closed. The thermometer will then show a decided decrease in temperature due to the absorption of the heat by the work. After lapse of a certain time, determined by the weight of the charge, the temperature will commence to rise again, and when it gets back to, say, 600 deg., where the thermometer stood when the work was inserted, the work is promptly removed.

It should be remembered that the thermometer will not indicate the precise temperature at which steel reaches a certain temper color under other conditions, but the temperature at which work will reach the exact temper color desired being once noted, the

FIG. 34.—GAS FORGE FOR KNIFE AND SHEAR BLADES.

furnace will perform the same work with the same degree of heat in the same time, so that the operator will then be able to turn out successive charges by simply watching the thermometer and a clock.

Gas Forge, for Knife and Shear Blades.

The construction of the furnace shown in Fig. 34 is similar to that of an oven furnace, but the firebrick slab upon which the work rests is ridged. These ridges form the partitions for the

FIG. 35.—BENCH FORGE.

heating of each blade separately. The slab is as wide as the entrance, and does not extend to the rear, but leaves a narrow slot through which the heat is forced from under the slab upward around the rear end of the slab and then forward in even volume to the vent, E, over the entrance.

In order to protect the points and thin ends of the blades, the corrugated slab may be covered as far as necessary by the firebrick slab, F, and thus heated by conductivity rather than direct action of the flame, while the thicker portions of the blades are directly subjected to it. The difference in the time required to heat the thin and the heavier portions of the blade is thus approximately equalized, and the whole blade heated uniformly to the exact degree required.

The cut represents a furnace made especially for shear blades from 8 to 12 inches long, and will accommodate 12 blades at a time, and will heat blades for forging or hardening as fast as they can be conveniently handled.

Bench Forge.

The bench forge shown in Fig. 35 is a handy little gas forge to be placed on the work bench, for forging and tempering small tools, heating the ends of rods or small pieces of metal of any kind. The heating space or chamber is $1\frac{1}{2}$ inches wide and high and 3 inches deep, heated evenly throughout by two side burners whose focus is in the center of the slot. Work can be placed over the slot and heated from below, or the slot can be covered by a slab shown in cut, and the heat confined to the chamber and raised to a very high degree quickly.

The forge can be permanently connected with gas pipe and air supply, or by rubber hose to be movable.

Gas is supplied through $\frac{1}{8}$-inch pipe, varies according to work done and quality of gas, and the amount consumed is too small to be considered when its work is taken into account.

Oven Furnaces for Annealing and Hardening.

Oven furnaces are used to heat a square or oblong space of any desired dimensions, evenly throughout, to any required degree of heat from a cherry red to a white heat, and especially to maintain any required temperature steadily for any desired length of time.

They will do the work of muffle furnaces perfectly except where an absolute seclusion of the work from the products of combustion is necessary. They are used for heating cutters, dies, reamers, shear blades, saws, and for annealing all kinds of metal work in quantities.

The annexed cut of oven furnace, Fig. 36, is typical of all oven furnaces except dimensions and the shape of entrance high. The entrance closed by the door, E, is 12 inches wide and 6 inches high. The firebrick slab, S, separates heating chamber above it.

The slab, S, covers the full length of the heating chamber from

front to rear, and is supported by small angle bricks located between the burners so as not to obstruct them.

The width of the slab is less than that of the interior of the
chamber, so that a slot is formed between the edges of the slab

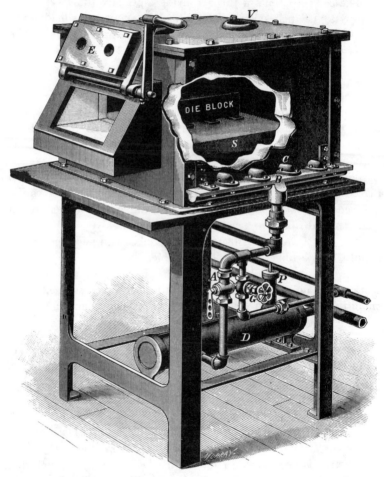

FIG. 36.—OVEN FURNACE FOR HARDENING AND ANNEALING.

and the side walls of even width throughout. The burners, C,
bolted to the distributing channel, B, are transposed with reference to the opposite series of burners, and arranged so that the
injected flames pass one another in opposite directions alternately. The injection of the fuel under pressure forces the heat

through the slots on each side of the slab, S, into the heating chamber above it, in even volume, and when the combustion chamber under the slab, S, has been heated up, the heat rapidly accumulates in the heating chamber. The products of combustion are released by the vent-holes, V, which being in the center, draw the heat upward from both sides, thus thoroughly heating the roof of the oven, from which the heat is reflected downward.

By the proportionate arrangement of all parts of the construction the heated chamber is evenly heated, and a block of steel placed as shown in the cut, will be heated up with perfect evenness simultaneously from all sides. The vestibuled entrance materially lessens the cooling-off effect produced by the opening door, E.

The gas supply and burners can be readily adjusted so that no flame whatever will be visible in the heating chamber, but as this would conduce to oxidation, the proportion of gas is indicated when a very small flame issues from the vent, V, after the furnace has become thoroughly heated. For all metal work the atmosphere in the heating chamber should be just visible by a "flimmering" effect, which indicates a non-oxidizing atmosphere.

The advantages of an oven furnace over a "muffle" consist in the more immediate and direct action of the heat upon the work, the lessened running expense by dispensing with costly and perishable muffles, and the adaptability of this furnace to very much larger work.

Case-Hardening Furnaces.

Case-hardening furnaces of the type shown in Figs. 37 and 38 are oven furnaces in construction, but being intended for work requiring the continuous application of higher heat, the linings are much heavier, and the entrance is closed by solid firebrick plugs, P, which are inserted and withdrawn by the cast iron carriers, D. As their name indicates they are mainly used for the process of case-hardening in cast-iron boxes, but also for annealing heavy steel dies, hubs, tool steel, etc. The slab which divides the combustion chamber from the heating chamber is heavier than in oven furnaces, properly supported by brickwork to bear heavy weights, and cast-iron rails are placed over the slab on which the boxes are removed in and out.

The burners, B, cover the whole length of the heating space; the opposite burners are connected to one gas and one air valve,

which control the supply. The door plug, P, is of the exact size
and thickness of the entrance, so that it can be easily inserted or
removed by cast-iron skeleton door, D.

The advantages of gas blast case-hardening furnaces are that
they do work more quickly and thoroughly than in the best of
coal ovens in use, because from the beginning of the operation all

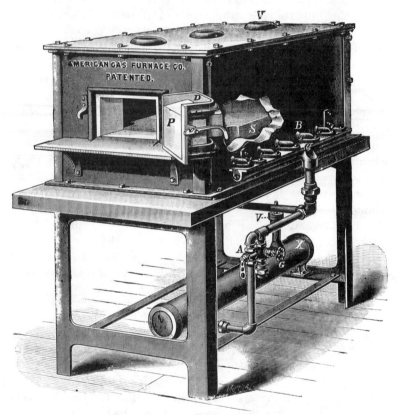

FIG. 37.— CASE-HARDENING FURNACE.

the boxes inserted—and all parts of each box—are heated simultaneously and alike, and that the heat can be kept constant at the
maximum degree which the cast-iron boxes will stand. These
advantages shorten the process materially, and when once the
time required for a given amount and kind of work has been ascertained, the same result can be produced thereafter, in the same
time.

Heating Machine for Hardening the Edges of Mower Blades.

The machine shown in Fig. 39 is used for hardening the edges of mower blades, and will operate as fast as the blades can be dropped into the jaws of the link belt K at I. The jaws are so formed as to expose only the edge of the blade as far as it is to be hardened, to the action of the heat, while the body of the blade is

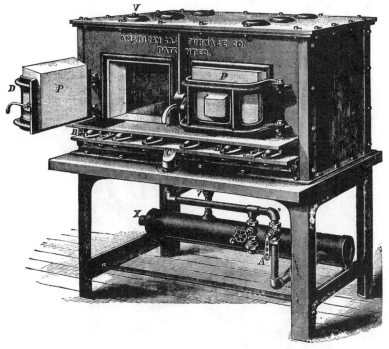

FIG. 38.—CASE-HARDENING FURNACE.

protected by the shape of the jaws as they close upon the blade before entering the heating chamber.

The speed of delivery is regulated by a countershaft with friction cone, placed above the machine and connected with the driving pull, H. The burners, B, emit a short focus flame from both sides and are under the perfect control of the gas valve, G, and the air valve, A. The jaws of the link belt open as they pass over the center of the sprocket at I, where the blades are inserted, closing just as they enter the furnace, and the blades pass through the heating space at the proper speed, first ascertained by a few pilot blanks run through the furnace, and are dropped into the cooling bath from the mouth, E, at the exact heat required for hardening the cutting edges.

The gas connects at union, G, and air, under a pressure of at least 1 pound to the square inch, at A. Where the machine is to be used on one uniform kind of blade, the proper speed may be experimentally obtained, and the friction cone countershaft dis-

FIG. 39.—HEATING MACHINE FOR HARDENING MOWER BLADES.

pensed with. Where the blades differ in thickness or size, a friction cone is indispensable.

Heating Machine for Hardening Cones and Shells.

In Fig. 40 is shown a furnace that is used for hardening cones, shells, pinions and similar small work, which can be stuck on the pins, which are inserted in the links of the endless chain. The work passes through the evenly heated furnace at a properly regulated speed and is discharged from the mouth, F, as fast as it is fed into the bath, T, without needless exposure to the air. The heat is under absolute control and the speed of the chain is adjusted to it so as to impart the exact temperature to the work required for proper hardening. When constantly used for the same work the proper speed of the chain is ascertained experimentally by turning the pull by hand and then speeding the machine ac-

FIG. 40.—HEATING MACHINE FOR HARDENING CONES AND SHELLS.

cordingly. When used for a variety of work countershaft with friction cone pulleys is needed.

Heating Machine with Revolving Trays.

The furnace shown in Fig. 41 is used for tempering needles, small blades, springs and screws. Its action depends upon heated air, with temperature so regulated that articles of irregular shape can be exposed to it long enough to impart the correct color or

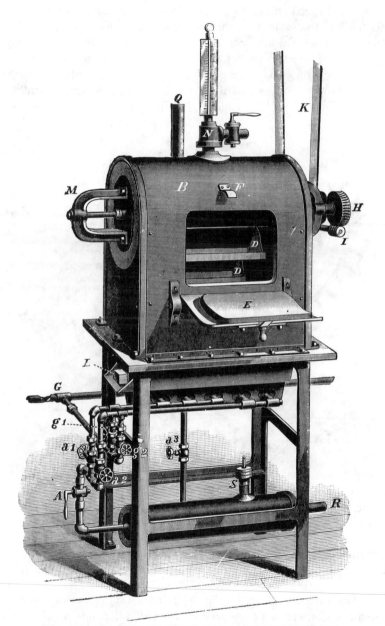

FIG. 41.—HEATING MACHINE WITH REVOLVING TRAYS.

temper to the heavier section, without overheating the thinnest and lightest part of the same piece. This is accomplished by regulation of the burner, which is usually divided into three sections, each under separate control. By these means the injection of the heat evenly throughout the furnace is easily secured, and the overheating of either end or the center is prevented. The burners heat an air chamber connected with the air drum by the pipe and valve A3, and heated air is distributed in the heating chamber through perforations in the top of the air chamber under light pressure, relieved through the vent cock at N. The work is placed in the pans, DD, which rotate at a speed of twice or thrice per minute, hanging loosely from rods connected with spokes around the driving shaft in the center, which receives motion from the worm gear, IH, connected with power. The door, E, is closed when furnace is charged with work, and opened for its observation. When open, the door forms a shelf or rest for the pans. The thermometer indicates a degree of temperature somewhat different from the actual heat in the furnace. Once tried for a certain temper of color, it is a perfect guide for repeating the same result.

Heating Machine for Small Parts.

The style of heating machine shown in Fig. 42 is used for heating large quantities of small steel work of uniform size and weight, evenly and uniformly, to any required degree for hardening, or for annealing the same, automatically. The work is placed on the cast-iron link belt, C1, which revolves entirely within the heating chamber, N, except where momentarily exposed at entrance, M, to receive the work. The burners, B, penetrate from each side of the furnace above the link belt, and are perfectly controlled by the gas valve, G, and the air valve, A.

The belt is supported by sprockets in the heating chamber, whose shafts revolve on the rolls, D. The belt is moved at required speed by means of a friction cone which is placed above the machine and connects with the driving sprockets, F, by the chains, HH.

The weight and size of the work, and the degree of heat which it requires, determine the speed at which the belt is moved, and consequently the output. The temperature of the heating chamber and the speed of the belt being under perfect control, the output is only limited by the time it takes to heat the work to the exact degree required.

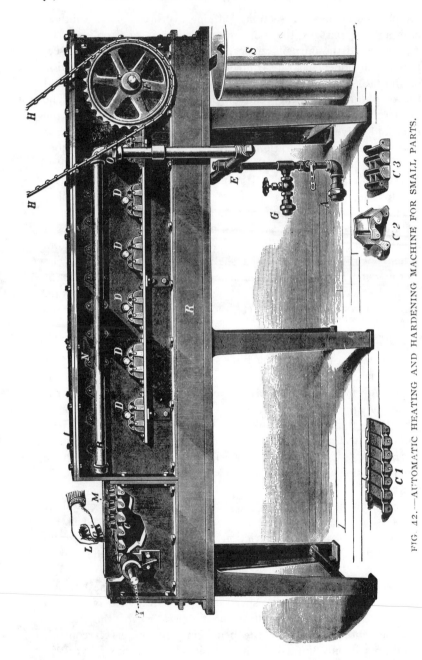

FIG. 42.—AUTOMATIC HEATING AND HARDENING MACHINE FOR SMALL PARTS.

The cooling part is not a part of the machine, but is shown merely to illustrate the whole operation. A proper cooling bath is important. It should be of ample size, and so arranged as to promptly cool the work without varying materially the temperature of the oil. Gas connection is made to the union, G, and an air blast from a positive pressure blower connects at A.

Barrel Heating Machine for Hardening Balls, Saw Teeth, Screws, Etc.

A type of machine designed for hardening quantities of bicycle

FIG. 43.—AUTOMATIC BARREL HEATING AND HARDENING MACHINE.

balls, but which has since been used for hardening detachable saw teeth, pens, nuts, bolts, screws, and other work not exceeding two and one-half inches in any dimension, is shown in Figs. 43 and 44.

Steel work of any shape is evenly and thoroughly heated to

the exact degree required, regardless of its shape, the thinnest and thickest parts being discharged at exactly the same temperature.

The machine is capable of heating from 1,500 to 2,000 pounds of steel work per day, the rate of delivery depending upon weight and shape of the piece.

The cooling bath marked X in the cut is merely a suggestion and its size depends upon the work to be done, as well as upon the available water supply for cooling. Its size and construction

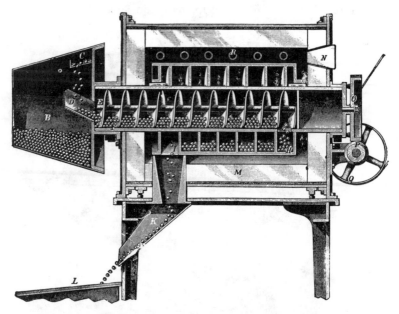

FIG. 44.—LONGITUDINAL SECTION THROUGH CENTER OF BARREL HEATING MACHINE.

also depend upon the temperature of the water to be used, and will vary under different circumstances.

Different methods are employed to cool oil baths. One is to draw the hot oil from the top, running it through pipes immersed in cold water, and pumping it back to the bottom of the tank cooled. Another is as illustrated. The tank holding the oil is shallow and water jacketed, the water being circulated at the rate required to keep the bath at proper temperature, determined by reference to a thermometer.

Where the water supply itself is not sufficiently cool, the bath may require cooling by ice, or the operation of the furnace may have to be limited to the capacity of the bath.

In several instances a machine of the type has heated work faster than it could be cooled, and the possible output therefore greatly depends upon the bath.

Construction and Operation.

The cylindrical body of the machine heavily lined with fire-brick incloses a solid cast-iron cylinder with a spiral way, 2¾ inches to 3 inches wide. The shaft of this "spiral way cylinder" is a heavy wrought-iron pipe containing the wrought-iron spiral, E. This hollow shaft and the cast-iron spiral cylinder revolve together. The heat is generated over the drum and is evenly distributed from both sides of the burners, R. The products of combustion are allowed to enter the spiral drum, thus excluding atmospheric air from it to prevent oxidation, and find their vent through the bottom of the furnace by being forced through the charge, I.

The work being placed in the hopper, B, which is kept filled to the level of the entrance, the scoop, C, revolving with the cylinder, fills itself with work as it is rotated downward, and empties its contents into the stationary funnel, D, when it rotates to a position above it. From this feeding funnel, D, the work drops into the spiral way, E, and is propelled to the opposite end of the inner spiral, where it drops into the outer cast-iron spiral way, H, in which it is propelled in the opposite direction and drops from the cylinder, I, to the chute, K, into the cooling bath, L.

The stationary feeding funnel, D, with the scoop, C, the interior spiral, E, and the cast-iron spiral drum, IH, revolve together by action of the worm gear, P O. The number of revolutions required to discharge the work at the proper heat are experimentally ascertained, and the rate of discharge being once established, the machine will turn out a perfectly uniform product.

The speed is regulated by a "friction cone" countershaft placed overhead, from which the power is transmitted to the pulleys, Q.

The furnace is lighted by withdrawing the plug, N, and turning on the air full, inserting a torch, and then turning on just sufficient gas, so that the burners emit a perfectly blue flame. The gas and air supply valves, A and G, permit the heat to be regulated to exact requirements. The temperature of the drum can be observed by the removal of the lighting plug, N, and by

means of the friction cone the time required for heating and delivery can be regulated with precision.

It will usually require from 45 minutes to one hour to heat the
spiral ways for hardening. At the expiration of that time the
machine will turn out the work at a regular rate. Where thin
and thick work are put through the machine together, the time of
delivery will be determined by the heaviest article put through,
but the lightest or thinnest will not be overheated unless the temperature is allowed to increase beyond the highest degree required
by hardening.

The main body of the machine is a solid fireclay cylinder inclosed by a heavy sheet-iron casing. All bearings are ball or
roller bearings, needing but little lubrication. Both heads of the
machine can be removed for the inserting of a new cylinder when
required, the body of the furnace resting independently upon the
table, thus remaining in position if heads are detached.

Heating Machine for Tempering and Coloring Steel.

A machine for tempering and coloring steel work in quantities
with perfect uniformity is shown in Fig. 45. The cut represents
an improved type of machine which has been in satisfactory operation for several years, for tempering and coloring pens, bicycle
chain link blocks, penholders, saw teeth, screws, buttons, and
other similar work not over two inches in any dimension.

The operation is performed by subjecting the work to the
action of sand or ground flint heated to the proper degree required for any grade of temper, and a bright, clean and perfectly
uniform temper color is obtained when the work has been properly
prepared for coloring by thorough cleansing.

The capacity of the machine depends upon the size and weight
of the articles, but as a criterion for its efficiency we can say that
we have witnessed bicycle chain blocks and insertable saw teeth
being put through at the rate of 150 pounds per hour.

The work is placed in the hopper, X, containing a small scoop,
which at every revolution deposits a measured quantity into a funnel leading into the heating drum. This drum, contained in the
main body of the machine, is provided with a spiral way which
gradually propels the work to discharge Z.

The spiral partitions are inclosed by a perforated cylinder,
through which sand or flint heated to the proper temperature to

obtain a desired temper or color is constantly sifted upon the work.

Provisions are made to keep a sufficient quantity of sand stored

FIG. 45.—HEATING MACHINE FOR TEMPERING AND COLORING.

above the work, so as to secure its even distribution into all the spiral divisions of the drum, thus effecting its uniform action upon the work.

The outer casing of the drum is subjected to an evenly distributed heat, controlled by proper adjustment of the gas valve, G, and the air valve, B.

The speed at which the work passes through the spiral drum is regulated by a friction cone placed above the machine, and the temperature by reference to the thermometer, I.

By noting the temperature at which different colors are ob-

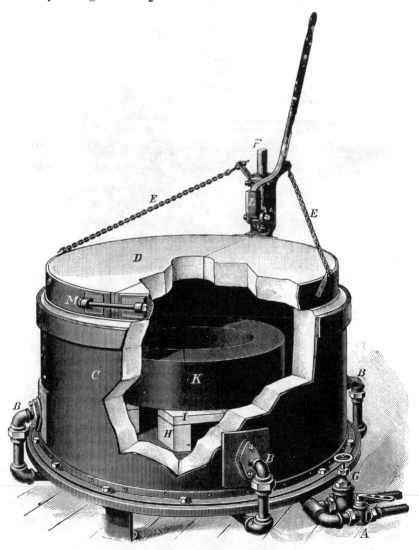

FIG. 46.—CIRCULAR ANNEALING AND HARDENING FURNACE.

tained by a given rate of delivery, the exact conditions of heat and speed under which a variation of color or temper is obtained can be readily observed and the perfect uniformity of the output assured.

Circular Annealing and Hardening Furnace.

The furnace shown in Fig. 46 is used for heating large rims, rings, discs, dies and other circular steel blocks which do not exceed 30 inches in diameter and 10 inches in thickness.

The illustration shows a circular block, K, resting upon the firebrick supports, H, so placed that they do not in any way obstruct the flames emitted from the four burners, B. The direction of the flame is tangential at the proper angle, to secure a rotary or whirling motion of the flame, and the even distribution of the heat, effecting the perfectly even heating of the work. This should be placed centrally, i. e., equidistant from the inner walls of the cylindrical casing.

The cover, D, is attached to the cover lift, and held by the adjustable chains, EE. It is lifted by a toggle joint by pulling the lever handle inserted in the socket, L, forward, and easily swings to either side. To replace the firebrick cover, the clasp, M, on the sheet iron belt which tightly incloses it is unscrewed, and a new brick lining inserted. The valve, G, admits gas and connects with the gas supply. A connects with air supply.

Oil Tempering Furnaces.

Furnaces of the type shown in Figs. 47 and 48 are used for tempering steel work in oil or tallow, and have the advantage over similar apparatus heated by coal that the heat is evenly distributed and penetrates the bath from all sides, that the temperature is under perfect control, that no flame can escape from the combustion chamber to ignite the oil or fumes arising from it, and that the temperature of the oil can be raised to an exceptionally high degree without risk of flashing. They are made in shapes and sizes to suit, round, square or oblong.

Furnace, Fig. 47, has the burners, B, arranged in two separate sections of four, two on each side, each section being under separate control of the gas and air valves below the distributing pipes, D and E, respectively.

To heat up the bath, both sets of burners are turned on, and when the desired temperature is reached, as indicated by the thermometer, L, one set of four burners can instantly be put out of use, so as to prevent the too rapid increase of the heat to the flash point.

The work is placed in the basket, K, which may be filled to the top. The immersion of the work in the bath quickly reduces its

FIG. 47.—OIL TEMPERING FURNACE.

temperature, and the work remains in the bath until the thermometer shows that the heat of the bath is restored in the proper degree. The best oil to be used is "Black Tempering Oil," generally supplied by the agencies of the Standard Oil Company, which can be raised to a temperature of 600 deg. F., and will temper steel from straw color to a light blue. The basket, K, is 18 inches long, 10 inches wide and 8 inches deep.

Oil tempering furnace, Fig. 48, in its construction is similar

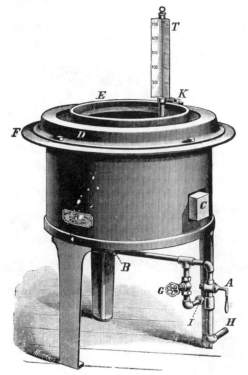

FIG. 48.—CIRCULAR OIL TEMPERING FURNACE.

to that of a soft metal furnace. The pot is 10½ inches in diameter, 10 inches deep, and the temperature is regulated by reference to the thermometer, T, held in place by the clamp, K. The bulb of the thermometer extends below the middle of the bath, and the burners are arranged to distribute the heat with perfect evenness around the pot.

For small work a wire basket is used to contain the articles to be treated, while larger work is suspended in the bath in any convenient way. The temperature being under the perfect control of the gas and air valves, G and A, the bath is heated until the thermometer shows the proper heat. When work is submerged in the bath it cools down, and the work remains there until the

FIG. 49.—HEATING MACHINE FOR HARDENING CHAIN.

temperature rises again to the original degree, when the work is removed.

Heating Machine for Hardening Chain.

This machine shown in Fig. 49 is one of many heating devices built for special purposes.

The idea successfully accomplished in this machine is to harden chains made from sheet steel, which passes from reel R1 first through the heating space into the cooling bath and is received on reel R2 perfectly and uniformly hardened.

By the accurate adjustment of burners and speed of travel a perfect uniformity in hardness of all the links is secured, the cooling bath is kept at a uniform temperature by proper circulation of the water or oil, which is drawn off the top, and after cooling is pumped back into the bath at the bottom. After the chain is hardened and wound upon the reel the whole reel is inserted in an oil tempering furnace to be drawn to the exact temper required.

Cylindrical Case-Hardening Furnace.

Furnaces of the type shown in Fig. 50 are used for case-hardening car axles of about 6 inches in diameter and not exceeding 8 feet in length.

The axle is inserted in the wrought-iron tube, R, having an interior diameter of 10 inches. The axle is placed in the exact center of the retort and the carbon packed tightly around it, after covering such parts as are not to be case-hardened with fire-clay or some other non-carbonaceous material. The retort being packed it is let down into the furnace from a suitable crane overhead, and the cover, K, put in position as shown, when the furnace is ready for operation.

The distribution of the heat evenly from the bottom to the top of the retort is effected by two independently controlled sets of burners; the lower set by the valves G2 and A2, and the upper set by the valves G3 and A3, while the common supply valves are G1 and A1. G stands in each case for gas and A for air.

The proper adjustment having been made on the lower and upper sets of the burners so as to secure an approximately correct distribution of the heat, the main gas and air valves are alone utilized to control the temperature, and the distribution of the heat properly over the whole length is then effected by the two vents, one in the bottom indicated by M2, and one on top in the

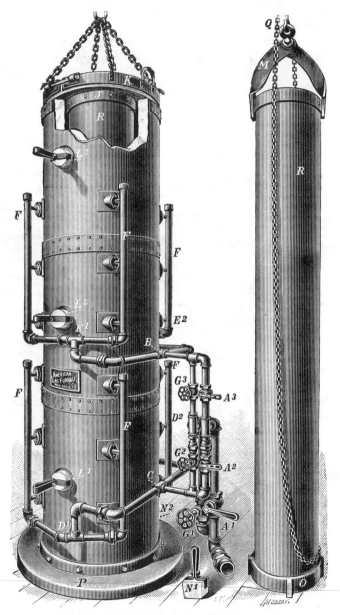

FIG. 50.—CYLINDRICAL CASE-HARDENING FURNACE FOR CASE
HARDENING CAR AXLES.

center of the cover, K. The top vent being closed entirely, the heat is driven downward and the products of combustion escape through the vent, N2. If N2 is closed and cover vent wide open, the heat is forced upward too rapidly, but by partly closing both vents, as much as will be found necessary from observation, **a**

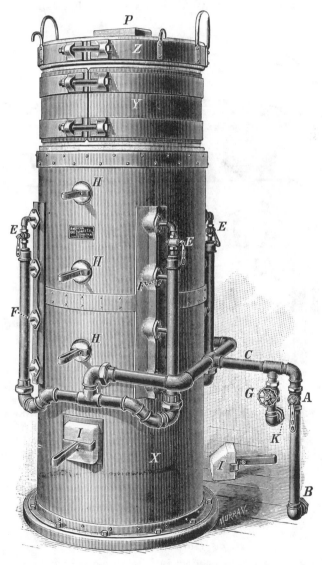

FIG. 51.—CYLINDRICAL CASE-HARDENING FURNACE.

perfectly uniform distribution of the heat is effected without a very close adjustment of the relative strength of the upper and lower burner tiers.

The regulation of the distribution by the vent holes is especially important when the temperature is to be raised quickly and the burners turned on as full as possible in both tiers.

Each row of burners has three burner tips, F, as shown, which

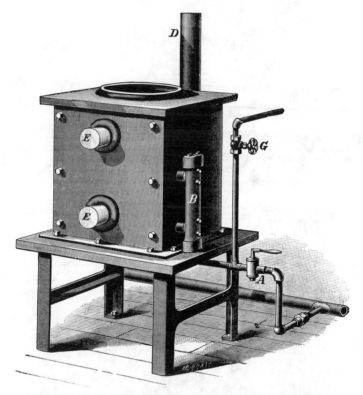

FIG. 52.—SOFT METAL FURNACE FOR LEAD HARDENING.

enter the cylinders from four sides at the proper angle to secure a rotary motion of the flame around the retort without impinging upon it. The body of the furnace contains three observation holes closed by the plugs, L1, L2, and L3. The lighting hole is not visible in cut but is indicated in the rear of the furnace by N2 and closed by the plug N1.

Lead Hardening Furnace.

The style of furnace shown in Fig. 52 is used for heating lead in black lead crucibles of any regular size for hardening steel work.

Any black lead crucible used for lead hardening must be regularly emptied after each operation. If the lead is allowed to cool and solidify, the crucible will crack when heated up again.

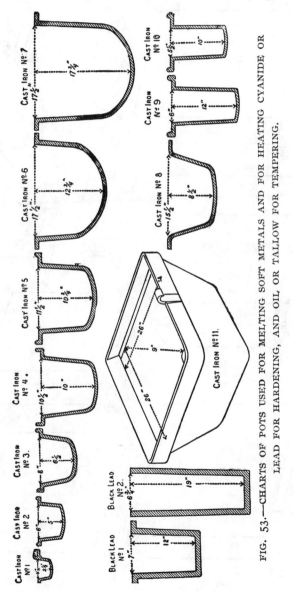

FIG. 53.—CHARTS OF POTS USED FOR MELTING SOFT METALS AND FOR HEATING CYANIDE OR LEAD FOR HARDENING, AND OIL OR TALLOW FOR TEMPERING.

Melting Pots.

Figs. 53 and 54 show charts of pots used for melting soft metals and for heating cyanide or lead for hardening, and oil or tallow for tempering.

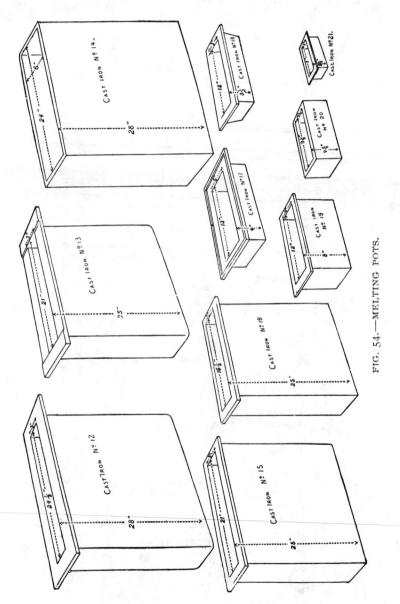

FIG. 54.—MELTING POTS.

Cyanide Hardening Furnaces.

The furnace shown in Fig. 55 is of a type used for heating steel work in cyanide of potassium for hardening; they are used by the leading bank note engravers in the United States for hardening transfer rolls and engraved plates, and by manufacturers

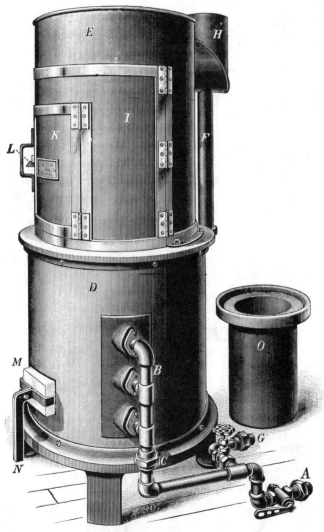

FIG. 55.—CYANIDE HARDENING FURNACE FOR CUTTERS, DIES, ROLLS, ETC.

for hardening cutters, dies, springs, and other steel work requiring a hardened surface. Their general features are also utilized in apparatus for heating chemical solution where the escape of

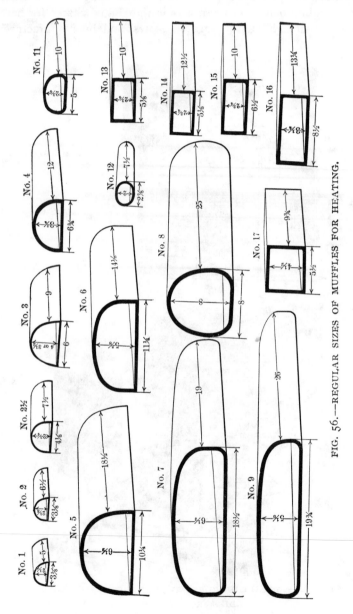

FIG. 56.—REGULAR SIZES OF MUFFLES FOR HEATING.

poisonous fumes from the pot or caldron into the room must be prevented. It contains a cast-iron or steel pot suspended by a flange with raised edge in the center of the heating chamber. The two opposite burners, BB, inject the flames into the space between the pot and surrounding firebrick lining, and heat the pot evenly without coming in direct contact with it. The two lighting holes in front are closed after the furnace is put in operation, and the products of combustion find their outlet in the pipe, E, which extends upward in the rear and enters the elbow on the sheet-iron pipe, S, passing the draft hole near the top of the hood, H. The heat from the combustion chamber is thus injected into the draft pipe, S, and a positive draft is created which carries off the fumes as they rise from the pot. Thus the poisonous fumes are carried off into the chimney, and with ordinary care none escapes into the room. Gas and air are indicated at G and A.

Regular Sizes of Muffles.

The annexed chart, Fig. 56, shows the regular sizes of muffles which are on the market. The number of the muffle corresponds to the number of the furnace, so that orders for the muffles can be given by the furnace number, or a furnace ordered by the number of the muffle.

The dimensions of muffles are their interior measurement.

Muffle Furnace.

The muffle furnace shown in Fig. 57 is typical of large sizes for heavy kinds of work requiring high heat. It is entirely encased in cast-iron framework firmly bolted together, with heavy linings and carefully trimmed and fitted fireclay sections. The casing is filled in above and around the arch with non-conducting material to lessen radiation, and the muffle bottom is protected by extra supports, as in oven furnaces, to prevent sagging under weight.

Tough Steel and Hard Steel—The Difference.

Although few mechanics seem to be aware of it, there is considerable difference between steel which is hard and steel which is both hard and tough, i. e., when a tool has been hardened and tempered to the degree thought best for the work which it is to perform and the edge does not stand up, but, instead, crumbles away, the steel is hard but is not tough and was heated wrongly in hardening, or was not quenched right. On the contrary, when a tool has been heated properly and hardened and tempered as it should be, it can be very hard and the edge will hold because for given degrees of hardness the same degree of toughness has been imparted during the heating and hardening processes.

FIG. 57.--MUFFLE FURNACE.

CHAPTER IV.

Judgment and Carefulness in Hardening.

As a great deal depends on the judgment and carefulness of the man who does the hardening in a shop, in all large manufacturing establishments the job of doing all the hardening should be given to one man. On this man's efficiency and judgment will depend the increasing or the reducing of the cost account, as one piece of steel which has been hardened properly will accomplish many times as much as a piece which has been hardened imperfectly. The manner in which the operator puts the steel into the quenching liquid will be responsible more than anything else, for having the pieces come out hard and free from cracks or deformities. Work with deep recesses will often have to go into the water with the recessed part first, or vise versa; according to the shape and location of the same.

When hardening large pieces which are worked out in the center, a stream of water striking against them is often absolutely necessary. There are some grades of steel which will give the best results if they are removed from the water as soon as the vibration has ceased and laid aside until cold. Experience, skill, and good sound judgment are necessary to do good hardening.

Successful Hardening.

In almost every establishment where any large amount of steel is hardened, some one man will be found who is considered an expert in the art. When such men really possess the required judgment and skill they are careful in the heating and quenching, and good results are attained. Very often, however, the man who is considered an authority on the subject, possesses very little real knowledge, but instead, through pure "gall" and "nerve," takes chances and either comes out on top or manages to cover up his mistakes. Beware of such men; they are responsible for more bad work in the shop than any others.

First and foremost, the effect of annealing on steel which is desired to be afterward hardened must be understood and appreciated. First, the annealing process softens and allows the steel to be worked into shape with ease. Second, it removes all strains sustained in the manufacture, such as rolling, hammering and forging. Thus experience teaches that it is necessary to anneal any odd shaped piece after all the surface scale has been removed and the piece roughed down.

Different Quenching Baths—Their Effect on Steel.

As, next to proper heating, more depends upon the quenching than anything else, it follows that the effects of the use of the various kinds of baths are required to be understood. The most generally used bath is usually cold water, though not infrequently

FIG. 58.—SCREW MACHINE SPRING THREADING DIES.

salt is added or a strong brine is used. The following will be found to answer well for the work mentioned: For very thin and delicate parts, an oil bath should be used for quenching. For small parts which are required to be very hard, a solution composed of about a pound of citric acid crystals dissolved in a gallon of water will do. For hardening springs, sperm oil; and for cutting tools, raw linseed oil will prove excellent.

Boiled water has often proved the only bath to give good results in a large variety of work, the parts requiring hardening being heated in a closed box or tube to a low red heat and then quenched. Sometimes the water should be boiling, at others quite hot, and then again lukewarm. Experience will teach the operator which is the best for special work. If a cutting tool such as a hollow mill, a spring threading die or a similar tool is to be hardened in a bath of this sort dip it with the hole up or the steam will prevent the liquid from entering the hole and leave the walls soft. A tendency to crack will also prevail if this is not done. The generation of steam must be considered when hardening work with holes or depressions in it, and attention must be paid to the dipping of the part so as to prevent the steam from crowding the water away. Clean water steams rapidly, while brine and the different acid solutions do not.

General Rules and Directions for the Hardening of Steel.

The effect of heat on steel is to expand it, even or uneven expansion depending upon the care and throughness of the heating operation. Thus if one part of a piece is heated quicker or higher than another the expansion is uneven, and the shape of the part changes to accommodate the local expansion. The consequence is that distortion takes place and remains permanent. In machine parts which have been finished and fitted or in any part which it is not practicable to grind afterward, the distortion often prevents the use of the piece, especially is this so in tools.

Distortion Through Uneven Heating.

We will suppose, for instance, that a part with a thin side or edge such as the cutter blade of the thread tool shown in Fig. 59, is to be hardened. To do this successfully the thin parts must be handled or manipulated in the fire so that the frail side

FIG. 59.—PATENT THREAD TOOL AND PARTS.

will not reach the hardening heat before the rest of the body of the piece, or it will become warped or distorted, this coming about, not through the difference of temperature of the various parts as some imagine, but, instead, through the more solid parts being too strong to permit expansion, and when expansion is at last accommodated it has been at the expense of the frailer part of the metal. From this it must not be inferred that the part having the smallest sectional area is the weaker while being heated, but instead that it is as strong as the rest except when at the same temperature. The following extracts from an article by the late Joshua Rose, M.E., in an early number of the *Scientific American Supplement,* explains this in a manner which leaves nothing to be desired:

"For example, suppose we have an eccentric ring, say ½ inch

FIG. 60.—SPECIAL ROUGHING TURRET REAMER.

thicker on one side than the other, and heat it midway between the thick and thin sides to a cherry red; while those sides are barely red-hot, the part heated to cherry red will be the weakest, and will give way most to accommodate the expansion, because the strength due to its sectional area has been more than compensated for by the reduction of strength due to its increased temperature. The necessity of heating an article according to its shape then becomes apparent, and it follows that the aim should be to heat the article evenly all over, taking care specially that the thin parts shall not get hot first. . . . If the article is large enough, the thin part may be covered, or partially so, during the first of the heating by wet ashes. If, however, the article is of equal sectional area all over, it is necessary to so turn it in the fire as to heat it uniformly all over; and in either case care should be taken not to heat the steel too quickly, unless, indeed, it is desirable to leave the middle somewhat softer than the outside, so as to have the outside fully hardened and the inside somewhat soft, which will leave the steel stronger than if hardened equally all through. Sometimes the outside of an article is heated more than the inside, so as to modify the tendency to crack from the contraction during the quenching, for to what degree the article expands during the heating, it must contract during the

FIG. 61.—TURRET TAP.

cooling. Whether the heating be done in the open fire or in a heating mixture, it must be done uniformly, so that it may be often necessary to hold the article for a time with the thick part only in the melted lead or other heating material; but in this case it must not be held quite still, but raised and lowered gradually and continuously to insure even heating.

The Hardening Fire and the Heat.

"The size of an article will often be an important element for consideration in heating it, because, by heating steel in the open fire, it becomes decarbonized; and it follows that the smaller the article in sectional area the more rapidly this decarbonization takes place. In large bodies of metal, the decarbonization due to a single heating is not sufficient to have much practical significance; but if the tool requires frequent renewal by forging, the constant reheating will seriously impair its value; and in any event it is an advantage to maintain the quality of the steel at its maximum. To prevent decarbonization for ordinary work charcoal instead of coal is sometimes used; and where hardening is not done continuously it is a good practice, because a few pieces of charcoal can be thrown upon the fire and be ready for use on a few minutes' notice. Charcoal should be used for the heating for the forging as well as for that for the hardening. Green coal should never be used for heating the steel for the hardening, even if it is for the forging process; because, while the steel is being well forged, its quality is maintained, but afterward the deterioration due to heating is much more rapid. A coke suitable for hardening should be made and always kept on hand. To obtain such a coke make a large fire of small soft coal well wetted and banked up upon the fire; and with a round bar make holes for the blast to come through. When the gas is out of the interior coal, and the outside is well caked, it may be broken up with a bar, so that the gas may be burnt out of the outside, and then the blast may be stopped and the coke placed ready for use at a moment's notice. Good blacksmiths always keep a store of this coke for use in making welding heats as well as for hardening processes. . . . If an article has a very weak part, it is necessary to avoid resting that part upon the coal or charcoal of the fire; otherwise the weight may bend it, and in heating long slender pieces they should bed evenly in the fire or furnace, or, when red hot, the unsupported parts will sag. In taking such pieces from the fire, the object is to lift the edges vertically so that the lifting shall not bend them; and this requires considerable skill, because it must be done quickly, or parts will become cooled and will warp, as well as not harden so much as the hotter parts.

Quenching for Hardening.

"We now come to the cooling or quenching, which requires

FIG. 62.—MILLING CUTTER.

as much skill as the heating to prevent warping and cracking, and to straighten the article as much as possible during the cooling process. The cooling should be performed with the view to prevent the contraction of the metal from warping the weaker parts; and to aid this, in cutters of the type shown in Fig. 62, tooth parts are sometimes made a little hotter than the more solid parts of the article, the extra heat required to be extracted compensating in some degree for the diminution of the sectional area from which the heat must be extracted. Water for cooling must be kept clean, and in that

FIG. 63.—STAY BOLT TAP.

case becomes better from use. It may be kept heated to about 100 deg. F., which will diminish the risk of having the article crack; any corners should be made as rounded as possible. If the water is very cold, and the heat hence extracted very rapidly from the outside, the liability to crack is increased; and in many cases the water is heated to nearly the boiling point, so as to retard the extraction of the heat. Since, however, the hardening of the steel is due to the rapid extraction of its heat, increasing the temperature of the water diminishes the hardness of the

FIG. 64.—SPIRAL LIPPED REAMER.

steel, and it is necessary to counteract this effect as far as possible, which is done by adding salt to the water. . . . All articles that are straight or of the proper form while leaving the fire should be dipped vertically and lowered steadily into the water; and if of weak section or liable to crack or warp, they should be held, quite still, low down in the water until cooled quite through to the temperature of the water. If the article is taken from the water too soon, it will crack, and this is a common occurrence, the cracking often being accompanied by a sharp, audible "click." Pieces of blade form should be dipped edgeways, the length of the article lying horizontally and the article lowered vertically and held quite still, because, by moving it laterally, the advancing side becomes cooled the quickest, and warping and cracking may ensue. Straight cylindrical pieces

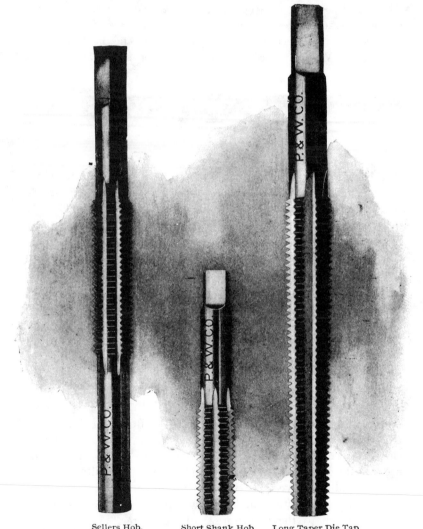

| Sellers Hob. | Short Shank Hob for Sizing Dies. | Long Taper Die Tap for Cutting Solid Dies. |

FIG. 65.—HOBS OR MASTER TAPS.

are dipped endwise and vertically. When, however, the dipping process is performed with a view to leave a sufficient heat in the body of the article to draw to a lower temper the part dipped, the method of proceeding is slightly varied."

The Hardening of Long Slender Tools.

In order to harden long slender tools, such as stay-bolt taps, "hob" taps and long, taper die taps, for instance, so as to not require subsequent straightening or grinding, care is necessary in the machining as well as the hardening operations. It is not desirable to use the highest carbon steel when a large tool is to be made if the hardening method given below is to be used.

Have the stock for the tool about ⅛ inch larger than the finish diameter and rough down to within 1-16 inch of size. Then pack in an iron box in powdered charcoal and reheat, heating to a red and being sure to heat evenly and slowly. This will remove all strains which may have taken place in the steel during the manufacture. The slower the steel cools the better will be the results in the hardening, as it may be heated to a lower heat which will have a tendency to refine it.

Sometimes when the rough-down blanks for long tools have been annealed by the method described above, upon taking them from the annealing box some will be found to have sprung. When this occurs do not attempt to straighten while cool, but instead, if possible, turn the bulge out. If this cannot be done, heat to a cherry red and straighten while hot and re-anneal. After finishing, test the tool for trueness, and then harden as follows:

Have a box large enough to allow the tools to stand upright and to leave lots of space for packing at the top, bottom and sides. Pack the packing material around tightly, put the lid on the box and heat thoroughly through, testing for heat with test rods, and when the proper heat is obtained hold it for a few hours, then remove the box and draw the tools carefully from the pack with a pair of tongs and quench in a bath of raw linseed oil which may be kept at a sufficient low temperature by some simple cooling arrangement.

When dipping the heated tools quench straight down into the center of the oil and move vertically until a black appears, when they may be moved to the edge of the bath tank. In an oil bath the contents should be agitated so that the oil will circulate and flow toward the center, thus keeping the vapor generated by contact of the heated steel and oil away from the work. By doing this there will be no soft spots in the work when hardened.

Hardening Small Parts and Long Thin Parts.

When a large number of very small parts, such as cutter blades of the type shown in Fig. 66, are to be hardened they

FIG. 66.—PATENT SQUARE THREADING TOOL.

should be packed in closed iron boxes, and the box heated. When all the parts have reached the proper heat, they should be dumped into the quenching bath, of either oil or water, as the nature of the work may require. Another way by which small parts may be heated uniform is by means of a lead bath. Keep

FIG. 67.—COMBINED DRILL AND COUNTERSINK.

the lead at the proper heat and cover the top with powdered charcoal and coke.

Very small tools, such as small piercing punches, etc., should be hardened in an oil bath or in luke warm water, as if cold water is used they will cool too quickly and come out of the bath cracked or so brittle as to be useless. Never heat a piece of steel for hardening hot enough to raise scale on it; even when it is a very large piece this can be overcome by heating very slowly in a packing box. When steel has been heated too hot and then quenched, the grain is rendered coarse and brittle, and, although it may be drawn to the desired temper, it will break quicker than

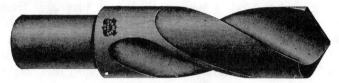

FIG. 68.—TWIST DRILL.

a piece which has been hardened at a very low heat and not tempered at all, although the piece which was heated too hot and hardened and drawn will be softer than the other piece.

When hardening long, flat or round objects they should be

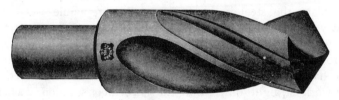

FIG. 69.—TWIST DRILL.

dipped endwise, holding them perpendicular with the surface of the bath. When this is done the articles will come out perfectly straight, or at least very little sprung. When dipped otherwise such tools will warp. When dipping a half-round tool dip it with

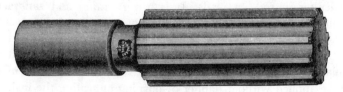

FIG. 70.—TURRET REAMER FOR FINISHING.

the half-round side at an angle of about twenty degrees with the surface of the water and it will come out either almost straight, or straight.

Hardening in Solutions.

In order to harden a large number of steel tools or pieces so that uniform hardness and temper will be attained, and so that the steel will come out of the process white and clean, as is often required, the following process may be adopted: First, in the heating of the steel, a solution which will project it from the fire and another to chill it quickly are necessary. This last solution will also give the desired clean white appearance to the steel. The receipt for this first solution is, equal quantities of sal-soda and borax in water containing one ounce of cyanide of potassium to the gallon. For the second solution, a strong brine made of salt and water, and about the same amount of cyanide as salt, will do. Have the water hot and add about two ounces of sulphuric acid to each gallon of water used; when mixed, put away in a cool place and keep well covered.

To use the solutions proceed as follows: Fill all holes near the edge of the steel with fireclay, then dip into the first solution and place the steel immediately on the fire while wet. Heat slowly and carefully and be sure not to heat any one portion of the work faster than another, as the slower the heat the more uniform its distribution in the piece. When the proper temperature has been reached, which should be a clear bright red, dip the work straight down into the hardening solution; when it has cooled, remove from the bath, and work of silvery whiteness and uniform hardness will be the result. When heating long slender pieces in this solution, dip them endwise, and do not shake about, but instead, revolve, if possible, rapidly.

Heating in Hot Lead for Hardening.

There is a large class of work which can be best heated for hardening in red-hot lead. It is a very rapid and satisfactory method for such tools as small counter-bores, reamers, shank, mills, knurls and parts such as bicycle cones, balls, cups, and sewing machine and typewriter parts. What makes the lead particularly valuable for heating such parts is that a uniform heat can be applied without danger of burning or scaling the inside before the center is heated.

When heating in lead a graphite crucible placed so that a uniform heat will be maintained beneath and around the pot will prove the best. As to the lead to use, care must be taken to get a brand with as little sulphur in it as possible. Never use scrap lead, as it will ruin the steel. Chemically pure lead should always be used.

There are a great many compounds in use to prevent the lead from sticking to the work. One of the best is the following: One pound of powdered cyanide dissolved in one gallon of boiling

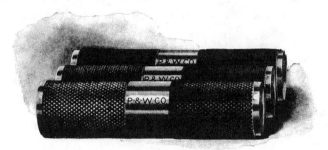

FIG. 71.—HEAVY KNURLS.

water; allow to cool, and then dip the articles to be heated in the solution; remove and allow to dry thoroughly before putting them into the lead. Moisture will make the lead fly.

Small articles of an even size and thickness throughout can be put into the lead cold, while irregular pieces must be heated

FIG. 72.—DOUBLE KNURLING TOOL.

nearly red before putting into the lead in order to prevent unequal expansion.

By keeping the surface of the lead covered with broken charcoal, drops will be prevented from forming. After the heating has been concluded empty the crucible.

To get good results when hardening by heating in lead, stir the liquid occasionally so as to equalize the heat, as the bottom will always be hotter than the top. When tools or parts with fine projections or teeth are heated, take a stiff brush and clean off any particles of lead which may stick in them before quenching. This is necessary as steel will not harden when lead has stuck to it, as the spots do not come in contact with the bath.

Hardening Metal Saws.

To harden metal saws or articles of a similar nature, provide a pair of flat cast-iron plates and oil the faces well with a heavy oil. Heat the saws in a box or some other arrangement which will prevent the fire from coming in contact with them (a flat plate will do) and prevent the article from warping during the

FIG. 73.—METAL SAW.

heating process. When heated to a bright red remove the article and place it on the lower oiled plate and drop the other plate on it quickly, and hold it down until the article is cold. If a pair of hinged plates are used one man can do the job; if not, two will be required.

Mixture to Prevent Lead from Sticking.

The formula here given is taken from the report of the Chief of Ordnance of the United States War Department, and is used when hardening files, and has also given good results when hardening small taps, milling cutters, reamers, broaches, rotary files and similar tools having fine teeth. The following is a copy of the report:

"Before hardening, the files are treated with a mixture of salt and carbonaceous materials to protect the teeth from decarbonization and oxidation. The kinds and proportions of the ingredients are given in the following table:

"Pulverized and charred leather..... 1 pound.
"Fine family flour...............∴ 1½ pounds.
"Fine table salt.................. 2 pounds.

"The charcoal made from charred leather should be triturated until fine enough to pass through a No. 45 sieve.

"The three ingredients are thoroughly mixed and incorporated while in a dry state and water is then added slowly to prevent lumps, until paste formed has the consistency of ordinary varnish. When ready the paste is applied to the file with a brush, care being taken to have the teeth well filled with the mixture. The surplus paste is then wiped off the file by the brush and the file is placed on end before a slow fire to dry. If dried too quickly, the paste will crack or blister; if not dried enough, the remaining moisture will be transformed into steam when dipped into the heated lead bath and cause an ebullition or sputtering of the lead, throwing out minute globules of the latter which may endanger the eyes of the operator. The fusing of the paste upon the surface of the file indicates the proper heat at which the file should be hardened."

Hardening Long Taper Reamers.

The hardening of long taper reamers of small diameter, so as to prevent them from coming through curved or twisted, is one of the most difficult operations for the hardener, and we can only advise the necessary precautions used by those who succeed with such work. The steel should be annealed a second time before the finishing cut is taken, by heating slowly in a low fire by packing it in an iron box or tube with powdered charcoal, fine sand, or clean ashes; then finished. The heating for hardening should be done in the same manner as the re-annealing. When the box and reamer have been heated thoroughly to a bright cherry red the reamers should be carefully drawn out endwise, so as to prevent the possibility of bending while hot; and immediately quenched vertically in an oil bath. Any variation from a vertical position while dipping is liable to warp the work, through one side cooling faster than the other. In drawing temper, care should be taken to heat evenly on all sides, so as to bring them to the same straw color, brown or light blue, according to whatever use the tool is to be put. Long delicate reamers should always be ground to size after the hardening and tempering operations.

The Use of Clay in Hardening.

Very often in die and tool work it is desired that a piece with a hole in the center should be hard around the outside and soft around the hole, or a punch is required to be hard at both ends and soft in the center. To accomplish these results with ease use clay in the following manner: When the stock around the hole is to be left soft and the outer edges of the piece hardened, fill the hole with clay and pad it at both sides, then heat the piece and plunge it into the water. When cool, remove the clay and the stock around the hole will be found to be soft while the edges will be as hard as required. To harden both ends of the punch and leave the center soft, put a bandage of clay around the center, or desired soft portion, about ¾ of an inch thick and bind it with a piece of thin sheet metal. Heat and quench, and the desired result will be accomplished.

When hardening dies or other press tools in which there are holes near the edges of the work, fill the holes with clay before heating and the tendency to crack will be overcome. When the holes are not filled with clay (when the steel is quenched) steam generates in the holes and cracks start, or excessive warping occurs, due to the fact that the steam does not escape fast enough and the contracting of the metal is unequal.

Special Instructions for Hardening and Tempering.

Often when tool steel is brought, special instructions will be given as to the method of hardening and tempering it. Sometimes these instructions are followed out and oftener they are not. Now in all cases when such instructions are given, don't forget to go by them, otherwise do not buy that brand of steel, but instead secure a brand which you can harden as you think best. There are various brands of steel on the market which are used for a number of special purposes and which possess qualities which other brands do not (in regard to cutting at high speeds, removing large amounts of stock, etc.) which require hardening at different temperatures and tempering at special colors. If you require this sort of steel for any special purpose, don't try to find out why the special instructions are given, but do as directed, and if the results are what the makers claim for it, it does not make any difference if you have to harden it in a cake of soap—the result is the thing.

Hardening and Tempering Round Thread Dies.

A good way to harden and temper round thread dies of the type shown in Fig. 74 is to proceed as follows: The die after having been drilled, worked, filed, etc., should be split at D, leaving about 1-32 inch of wall as shown. Heat carefully and quench in water bath, after which polish the sides. To temper use the lead bath. Enter the die into the bath edgeways up to about the dotted line shown in Fig. 74. After holding it in the bath for about a minute re-

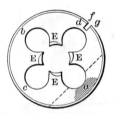

FIG. 74—THREAD DIE.

move and examine. If the heating has been done correctly the part A will have turned blue while the point E will not be drawn at all. Treat B likewise, and in turn C and D. When this is done properly there will be sufficient heat contained in the outer portion to gradually draw and temper the point E, which may be anything from a light yellow to a dark yellow, as the case may require. In the tempering, a few drops of lard oil on the teeth at intervals when required will check the temper and prevent it from running out further at one point than another. A little practice will teach the operator how much heat to subject the outside portion of the die to so as to allow of all the point E coming to the same temper.

After the tempering process the die may be repolished and then the wall left at D removed by grinding with a thin emery wheel, or by entering a small narrow face set and hitting it a sharp blow, when the wall will break out. The reason for leaving the thin wall at D is to hold the ends firm while hardening, thus preventing excessive shrinking and warping. Split bushings may be hardened in the same manner.

Hardening Bushings, Shell Reamers, Hobs, Etc.

A device useful in the hardening of bushings, shell reamers,

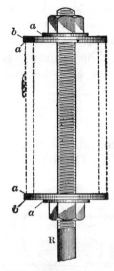

FIG. 75.—USEFUL
HARDENING DEVICE.

hobs, etc., is shown in Fig. 75, and consists of a piece of drill rod, R, threaded about an inch longer than the length of the article to be hardened, and nut and washer located as shown. The dotted lines show the work to be hardened, AAAA, asbestos washers, BB, common iron washers, the whole being held together between the two nuts. Heat the entire arrangement to the proper temperature and quench in water in the usual manner. By using a device of this sort an upward flow of water through the article is prevented, as is the consequent sudden chill, thus eliminating to a certain extent the tendency to warp or crack. In such tools in which the outside only is desired to be hardened, the method is an excellent one, as the inside will remain comparatively soft, unless very thin, when it will harden clear through.

Hardening and Tempering Collet Spring Chucks.

The following kink we have found very handy when making collet spring chucks of the shape shown in Fig. 76. After finishing them in the lathe, leaving, of course, enough stock to lap and grind to a finish, face them on an arbor and saw the spring slots as shown; that is, at the end of each slot, as shown at T and V. Instead of cutting completely through at this point, leave a very thin wall about ⅛ inch long at the end of the cuts. Then harden and temper the chucks as desired, and after lapping the inside to size, place on an arbor and grind the tapers as required; then take a small, narrow broach and by entering it into the slots and hitting it a sharp blow with a hammer the thin wall will break through. This kink I have used to the best advantage in shops which had no grinding facilities. When proceeding as aforesaid it was possible to finish the outside and taper to size before hardening without the possibility of the chucks running out to any noticeable extent. Of course for

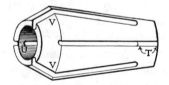

FIG. 76.—SMALL COLLET
SPRING CHUCK.

work of the utmost accuracy this method would not do. But then again work of the utmost accuracy is not accomplished in shops where the tool facilities are not up to date.

The Taylor-White Process for Treating Steel.

In the September, 1901, number of the Journal of the Franklin Institute was published a paper by Charles Day upon the Taylor-White process for treating tool steel, and the results obtained with steel so treated, at the works of the Link Belt Engineering Company, Philadelphia, Pa. When this process was first announced facts were given and quoted reports of tests made at the works of the Bethlehem Steel Company, Bethlehem, Pa., where the process was developed by Messrs. Taylor and White. The paper by Mr. Day gives information upon air hardening steels in general before reverting to the subject of steel treated by the Taylor-White process.

Mr. Day says that air-hardening steels have unquestionably replaced the carbon variety for roughing work, the efficiency of the former ranging from one and one-half to twice that of the latter. This gain is because air-hardening steels hold their cutting edge at much higher temperatures than carbon steels and consequently can be worked at proportionately greater cutting speeds. The usual method of hardening air-hardening steels is well known, manufacturers usually placing a great stress on the fact that the tool must be heated over a cherry red, otherwise it will be burned and so ruined. The object of Messrs. Taylor and White was to obtain some exact knowledge on this matter, and extensive experiments were conducted in the belief that a tool steel could be produced to give still better results than those already obtained.

The new process depends upon the fact that although both carbon and air-hardening steels deteriorate rapidly when the temperature rises above a cherry red, there are some chemical compositions that may be used for air-hardening steels which are much improved as cutting tools if they are raised to a higher temperature in the hardening process. Their maximum efficiency is reached when the steel is heated to a point where it crumbles when tapped with a rod. The point to which air-hardening steel was formerly heated in the process of hardening is between 1,500 and 1,600 deg. F., and is called the breaking-down point. Steel having the new treatment is heated to 2,000 deg. F. The composition found to give the best results consists of an air-harden-ing steel containing about 1 per cent of chromium and 4 per cent of tungsten; while for very hard metals, such as the chilled scale on cast-iron, etc., 3 per cent of chromium and 6 or more per cent of tungsten are good. The variation in carbon seems to matter but little, steel varying from 85 to 200 points giving equally good results.

The tool is cooled rapidly from the "high heat" (2,000 de-grees) to a point below the breaking-down temperature, in a lead bath, and then slowly in the air, or lime, etc., as the case may be. It is essential that at no time the temperature should rise, as in such a case the tool would be seriously impaired. After the steel has cooled off, its efficiency is found to be further increased by subjecting it to what is termed the "low heat" for about ten minutes; this temperature ranging from 700 deg. to 1,240 deg. F. After cooling from the "low heat" the tool is ready for use. It is not essential to anneal the steel when reforging and the tools can be worked with comparative ease.

In the operation of the Taylor-White process apparatus is employed by means of which temperature can be controlled within very narrow limits, which accounts for the uniformity of results obtained with the tools treated by this process.

About 97 per cent of the material worked upon at the shops of the Link Belt Engineering Company is cast-iron. In order to make a rough test on cast-iron one tool was obtained from Bethle-hem and put to work on a 7-foot boring mill turning the inside of a cast-iron ring. The time required to do this work with their old tools had been determined many times in setting piece rates, and was about fourteen hours. With the Taylor-White tool the time was reduced to three and one-half hours, and a gain of 75 per cent made. While steel used heretofore was not the best ob-tainable, and was probably not worked to its highest efficiency, there was, nevertheless, a large saving due to the new steel.

Some interesting data was also obtained from an order of rope sheaves, the time required on similar work having been tabu-lated for several years. The average time required to machine thirteen sheaves with the old tools was nine and one-half hours; the same for sixteen similar sheaves, the roughing being done by Taylor-White tools, was five hours and five minutes, or a saving of 46½ per cent.

Assuming, however, the time for setting up, forming, boring

and polishing the same when the sheaves were finished with old tools as with the treated tools, since the latter are not suitable for cutting finishing cuts, the time for roughing would have been 7.85 hours and a saving of 56.3 per cent was made in operations where it was possible to use treated tools.

In order to obtain some data with regard to pressure on the points of tools for given depth of cuts, feed, etc., and at the same time to show the effect of the treatment, a cast-iron ring six and one-half feet in diameter was bolted to the table of a seven-foot mill. The first tool used was one treated for hard material. It cut 106 pounds of metal in 10 minutes, and when removed was in perfect condition. A "Mushet" tool under the same condition lasted but one minute, and removed 5½ pounds of metal. The actual pressure against the tool in each case exceeded 3¼ tons, while the pressure per square inch with another self-hardening tool was 143,000 pounds.

Eighteen months ago a 50 horse power engine supplied the power for about 40 machine tools in the Link Belt Engineering Company's works, and also run the pattern shop and grinding room. The actual horse power developed had been found to average 45. Of this 27 horse power was consumed by the shafting, leaving but 18 horse power for actual work. After the new tools were in general use and the machine pushed to obtain the desired results, it became apparent that the power was absolutely inadequate; indicator cards from the engine frequently showed an overload of 60 per cent, and at this point it was found essential to put motors on some of the larger tools.

The following particulars about the process have been furnished by the Bethlehem Steel Company:

"The practical speeds at which these tools will run has been found to be from two to four times that of any steels which we have experimented with, and we have endeavored to obtain the best in the market.

"The process, which is applied after the tool has been dressed or machined to shape, penetrates to the center of the steel, even in the largest tools we have ever treated, i. e., 4 inches square. All of the standard brands of self-hardening steel which have been experimented with are improved to a more or less extent by the treatment; it is preferred, however, to use a steel of special composition in order to get the greatest uniformity and maximum results. This special steel forges so much more readily than the general run of self-hardening steels that tools of different shapes may be easily made up.

"We have also discovered a simple and comparatively rapid method of annealing of special steel, by which tools may be easily machined to shape, making it applicable to twist drills, chasers, inserted cutters, etc., which have theretofore not been made from self-hardening steel.

"A great advantage in the use of these tools is that when cutting dry at the rate of maximum efficiency the chips should come off blue. These blue chips enable a foreman at a glance to tell whether the work is being done at the proper speed when running under water at the proper cutting and allowing the tool to cut dry for a few moments.

"The apparatus used in the Taylor-White process offers also a simple and effective means of heating any other tools at uniformity and higher qualities in this class of steel, as well as self-hardening steel.

"As is well known, tempering steels of different makes and different qualities require different temperatures for hardening to obtain the best results; therefore, by means of our apparatus, which is capable of closely controlling temperature, these points may be accurately determined for each class of steel, and made use of in daily practice. The operation of the process is extremely simple, as it is controlled by apparatus which regulates the different steps, and does not require skill or expert labor."

CHAPTER V.

Tempering.

In the term "tempering" we include all processes which tend to reduce the hardness of steel to a degree recognized inside the color test by color, and also all processes by which the degree of hardness is lowered, modified, tempered, or lessened. It is wrong to apply the term "temper" to processes which at one operation leave the steel harder than any degree of the color test; a process which does not reduce the hardness of steel to a degree denoted by some color in the color test should be termed hardening.

If instead of the color, in tempering, the degree of temperature required were given, the process would be very much simplified. Thus 430 degrees would denote the same degree of hardness as a faint yellow and all degrees of hardness above that would have to be specified in less temperature, while all degrees of softness down to a blue tinged with green would be included in degrees of temperature up to 630. The degrees of softness below that denoted by color test or thermometer are: bright red in the dark, 720 degrees; red hot in twilight, 884 degrees, and red visible by day, 1,077 degrees. The degrees of softness below them are indistinguishable by the test; they remain unknown quantities of degrees, and are only indicated by the ease with which the metal can be machined.

The universal adoption of thermometer test for tempering will remove the technical objection to the color test, i. e., that the color obtained on the piece of steel through heat is no indication that the steel possesses any above its natural degree of hardness; as steel, wrought iron and cast iron will assume, when polished and heated to the necessary degree of temperature, all the colors of the test. Thus the color on a piece of steel is simply an indication that it has been heated to a certain degree, not that it is tempered, or in fact that the heating process has in any way changed the degree of hardness or softness.

Tempering when done by a second operation modifies the hardness imparted to the steel by the first one and depends for its uniformity upon the uniformity of the first process. For instance, if a number of pieces of steel of uniform grade are heated to the same degree of temperature, and quenched in water until cold, then removed, then tempered to the same color, they will of course be possessed of an equal degree of hardness; but if other pieces of steel of a different carbon percentage are subjected to exactly the same process in all its details, leaving upon them the same temper color, they will not possess the same degree of hardness as those of the first lot. From this we learn that temper colors may be proof of equality in the degree of temper in pieces of the same steel, but the same is not indicative of any uniform degree of hardness in different steels.

In the hardening of inexpensive cutting tools the above facts make very little difference, as for such tools special brands of steel are procurable which will harden sufficiently to give accuracy to the color test of tempering, when heated to any degree of heat from a blood red to a yellow red; the difference in hardness in the steel when quenched at either degrees of heat being too small to entitle them to consideration in tools which are inexpensive to make.

In the tempering of special tools the exact degree of temper which experiment has determined must be given. A tool user knows that in the shade of yellow in the color test alone enter over a range of 70 degrees, and that within these 70 degrees lies a wide range of hardness. It is much better to adopt a tempering process that will determine with accuracy the first heating temperature, as, for instance, the heating of a tool in melted lead, melted salt, or melted glass and then quenching it into a cooling bath the temperature of which may be maintained by suitable means, and then drawing the temper in a bath of oil heated to and maintained at the degree of temperature required. When such methods are used, if the steel used is of a brand which experience in using has taught to be uniform, the greatest obtainable accurate degree of temper will be obtained in both the operations, and the tools will be hardened better and more reliable than could be obtained under the color test.

In most establishments where large numbers of hardened tools or parts are required the methods described are in use; but when the articles are large or only a few small parts at intervals are required, it would not of course pay to keep the heating arrangements constantly ready. It is then that the open fire and the color test must be adopted. It is under the latter conditions that the skill, experience, and judgment of the hardener are called into use, as from the time the steel is put in the fire until it is quenched and tempered, upon him depends absolutely the entire success of the operations.

Tempering in the Sand Bath.

When a number of pieces of the same size or of slightly different sizes have been hardened and it is desired to draw them all to the same temper, the sand bath will be found to give the most uniform results. This consists of an iron box filled with sand and heated over the fire or in a muffle to the temperature required. When the sand has been heated to the required degree, the tools to be tempered are lowered into it and removed when the color denoting the temper required appears.

The Effects of Slow Heating and Tempering.

Always remember that the slower the temper is drawn, the tougher the steel will be. When steel is slowly heated in tempering and the heat is distributed equally over the entire piece, the molecules assume the most stable position with regard to each other, and when the tool is in use, all are alike affected by any shock sustained. The effects of heat on copper and bronze are exactly opposite to those manifested by steel, as when such metals are cooled slowly they become brittle and hard, but when cooled rapidly soft and malleable.

Tempering in Oil.

Almost all large shops in which any amount of hardening and tempering are done have discarded the method of tempering by colors and have adopted the more reliable methods of doing it in oil, gaging the heat by thermomenter. A kettle containing the oil is placed on the fire and heated to the right temperature; the hardened parts are thrown in and left in the liquid until drawn. By this method there is no possibility of overdrawing, as it is impossible for the parts to become hotter than the oil. When tempering in this manner it is not necessary to brighten the work before the operation, and when a lot of such work is done it will be accomplished much cheaper than if the old method were used; besides, the most satisfactory results will be attained.

Hardening and Tempering Springs.

As very often springs are included in the constructions of fixtures, appliances, and machines, it is well to understand how to harden and temper them successfully. For small and medium-sized springs use a solution composed of one-half sperm oil, one-half neat's foot oil with an ounce of rosin, and the springs will come out of the bath tempered as desired. For heavy springs, which have to exert a great deal of pressure, use hot water. Have the water boiling and plunge the springs, when at the proper heat, into it. By adopting this method no burning off will be necessary, as the springs will be the proper temper. What is more, they will not break or "crawl up" when in use.

Blazing Off Springs.

To temper springs by "blazing off" use cottonseed oil. For some work, however, a mixture of this and fish oil will work better than either of the two oils alone. In doing this work experiments will determine just what oil or what proportion of a mixture of the two will contribute to attaining the best results.

Tempering Rock Drills in Crude Oil.

For the tempering of rock drills crude oil will give the best results, and by using it as a quenching bath even the amateur may temper steel to stand like an expert. This is so because when using oil a slight variation in temperature does not produce the effect on steel that water does. The experience with crude oil

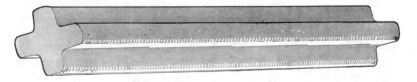

FIG. 77.—ROCK DRILL STEEL.

for the tempering of rock drills by one who understands the requirements of such work is of value and may cause its more extensive use. B. Hastings, in the Mining and Scientific Press, states:

"It is a very rare thing for an oil-tempered drill to break, and it wears much better than a water-tempered one. The most serviceable slack tub I found to be common five-gallon oil can, with the top left as a flap or cover to throw down and smother flame in case the oil ignites from the hot steel. If the vessel is left open the ignition, if it does occur, is of little consequence, like that of coal tar; but with a partially closed tub or tank can, the accumulated gases are liable to produce 'fireworks,' as the writer can testify. There is really no necessity for such inconvenience, however, as the proper heat for plunging the steel—a bright red—is a little below the point necessary to flash the oil. I do not use more than five inches of oil in the bottom of the can. The hotter the oil becomes, the better are the results. The consumption of oil is small, principally due to that portion sticking to the drills on withdrawal. Plunging them in loose dirt afterward will clean them."

Hardening and Tempering Mill Picks.

Bath for Hardening.—Take 2 gallons rain-water, 1 ounce corrosive sublimate, 2 of sal-ammoniac, 1 of saltpeter, 1½ pints of rock salt. The picks should be heated to a cherry red, and cooled in the bath. The salt gives hardness, and the other ingredients toughness to the steel; and they will not break, if they are left without drawing the temper.

Composition for Tempering Cast-Steel Mill Picks.—To 3 gallons of water add 3 ounces each nitric acid, spirits of hartshorn, sulphate of zinc, sal-ammoniac, and alum; 6 ounces salt, with a double handful of hoof parings; the steel to be heated a dark cherry red. It must be kept corked tight to prevent evaporation.

To Temper Picks.—After working the steel carefully, prepare a bath of lead heated to the boiling point, which will be indicated by a slight agitation of the surface. In it place the end of the pick to the depth of 1½ inches, until heated to the temperature required. The principal requisites in making mill picks are: First, get good steel. Second, work it at a low heat; most blacksmiths injure steel by overheating. Third, heat for tempering without direct exposure to the fire. The lead bath acts merely as a superheater.

Straightening Hardened Pieces Which Have Warped.

When a piece of steel has been carefully heated and just as carefully quenched, there is little chance of its warping. But when a piece does warp, before it can be used for the purpose required, it must be straightened. To do this proceed as follows: Take two "V" blocks and place them on the bed of an arbor press or a straightening press—either one will do—and place the piece or tool on the "V" blocks with the concave side down. Then take a Bunsen burner, with a hose attached to it for the gas supply, and heat the concave side; do this slowly, and do not heat hot enough to draw the temper. While the steel is hot apply sufficient pressure to spring the piece or tool back into shape. A large number of hardened pieces, which would otherwise prove useless, may be saved by straightening them in this manner.

Tempering Thin Articles.

Articles of thin material, like springs, which require a spring temper, are frequently treated by dipping in oil and then burning off the oil over the fire. Blacksmiths adopted this method instead of trying to temper by watching the color, as it is found that it subjects the piece to just about enough heat to produce the desired results. In the case of thicker pieces, however, like tools, it is much better to use the hot iron and watch the color. The temper can thus be drawn to just the point desired, and the steel will be tempered more uniformly both on the outside and inside than when the other method is used.

Tempering in the Charcoal Flame.

A great many mechanics prefer to temper in a charcoal flame. To do this properly the thickest portion, or the part not requiring any temper, should be held in the flame; and as it becomes heated, the tool should be wiped at intervals with an oily piece of waste. The oil will keep the temper even and prevent drawing more in one place than in another. In drawing the temper of any tool it should always be done slowly, as if it is done rapidly the temper is apt to run out before one is aware of it.

Tempering Wood Planer Knives.

The following extract from an article contributed to the "Woodworker" gives a practical method for tempering wood planer knives:

"We have one batch of knives that will not hold an edge in oak unless drawn to a temperature of about 400 degrees, and as this shows a very indistinct color it is not easy to get without a thermometer. As these are 6, 8, and 10-inch knives, they cannot be hardened in water without a reasonable certainty of cracking back the length of the bevel in one or more places; and as oil will not carry off the heat fast enough to keep the body of the knives from drawing the edge, it promised a serious problem to solve. This was managed in the following manner, and after a few trials I was able to obtain the proper degree of hardness without drawing for temper at all.

"Take a vessel of proper width to receive the length of knife, put some water in the bottom and pour an inch of oil on top. Heat the edge of your knife an even cherry red back as far as you wish to harden it, and holding it level thrust the edge into the oil for a moment until the color leaves, then slowly let it down into the water. The oil cools without cracking, and the water prevents the heat in the body from drawing the edge. It is not necessary to harden all long knives in this manner, as the oil alone will produce a sufficient hardness in ordinary cases if a large enough body of oil is used and the edge of the knife is immersed with a stirring motion. It can then be tempered to about 500 degrees by the heat of the body of the knife and suddenly cooled in water at about 80 degrees. These long knives are pretty sure to warp some when tempering or hardening in this way, the back or soft steel side contracting more than the face. To straighten, lay face down on an anvil and with a round-nosed machinist's hammer give a quick, sharp blow, distributed evenly between the back edge bevel and the line of front end of slots. Be careful to hammer directly over the spot resting on anvil or the knife will vibrate in the hand and the force of the blow will be diffused and lost. This gentle hammering stretches the back of the knife, and when its length equals the face it will be straight."

Tempering Swords and Cutlasses.

The tempering of swords so that they will stand the United States government test may be accomplished by heating in a charcoal fire to a bright red and quenching in pure water, afterward drawing the temper in a charcoal flame.

Drawing Polished Steel Articles to a Straw Color or Blue.

The surface of polished steel articles will acquire a pale straw color at 460 degrees F., and a uniform deep blue at 580 degrees F. The other shades between these may be had at intermittent temperatures.

Tempering Solutions.

1. Saltpeter, sal-ammoniac and alum, of each 2 ounces; salt, 1½ pounds; soft water, 3 gallons. Never heat over cherry red; draw no temper. Sal-ammoniac and iron turnings or filings make good rust joints.

2. To 6 quarts of soft water add 1 ounce of corrosive sublimate and two handfuls of common salt. When dissolved the mixture is ready for use. The first gives toughness, the latter hardness to the steel. Remember this is deadly poison.

3. Water, 3 gallons; salt, 2 quarts; sal-ammoniac and saltpeter, of each 2 ounces; ashes from white ash bark, 1 shovelful. The ashes cause the steel to scale white and smooth as silver. Do not hammer too cold. To avoid flaws do not heat too high, which opens the pores of the steel. If heated carefully you will get hardness, toughness and the finest quality.

4. Salt, 4 ounces; saltpeter, ½ ounce; pulverized alum, 1 ounce to 1 gallon of soft water. Heat the articles to a cherry red, and quench, but do not draw temper.

5. Saltpeter and alum, each 2 ounces; sal-ammoniac, ½ ounce; salt, 1½ ounces to 2 gallons of soft water. Heat parts to be tempered to a cherry red and quench.

Tables of Colors, Melting Points and Suitable Tempers for Given Tools.

The following tables have been carefully arranged and will be found to be approximately correct:

Melting Points of Solids.

	Deg. F.
Aluminum	1,157
Antimony ....from	811 to 1,150
Bismuth ....from	476 to 512
Copper ....from	1,929 to 1,996
Lead ....from	608 to 618
Mercury	— 39
Tin ....from	442 to 451
Zinc ....from	680 to 779
	Wr't"
Cast iron..	2,477
Gold	2,587
Silver	1,250
Steel	2,501
Glass	2,377
Brass	1,897

Melting Points of Solids—Continued.

	Wr't"
Platinum	3,077
Cadmium	602
Saltpetre	600
Sulphur	225
Potassium	135

Table of Tempers to Which Tools Should be Drawn, Arranged Alphabetically.

Tool.	Color.	Deg. of Tem. F.

A

Augers	Light purple	530
Axes	Dark purple	550
All cutting tools for soft material	Very light yellow	420
All hand taps and dies	Straw yellow	460
All kinds of hand reamers	Straw yellow	460
All percussion tools for metal	Blue	549

B

Bone-cutting tools	Very pale yellow	430
Boring cutters	Straw yellow	460
Butt mills for brass	Very light yellow	420
Burnishers	Very light yellow	420
Bending and forming dies	Dark yellow	490

C

Chasers	Straw yellow	460
Coppersmiths' tools	Light purple	530
Cold chisels for steel	Light purple	530
Cold chisels for cast iron	Dark purple	550
Cold chisels for wrought iron	Light purple	530
Circular saws for metal	Light purple	539
Cutting tools for iron	Light yellow	440
Collets	Dark yellow	490
Chuck jaws	Dark yellow	490
Chisel for wood	Spotted red-brown	510
Clutch bolts	Very dark blue	601
Cams with sharp corners	Very dark blue	601
Clutch springs	Blue	549

D

Drifts	Brown yellow	500
Dental and surgical instruments	Light purple	530
Drawing mandrels	Very light yellow	420
Drills for brass	Straw yellow	460

E

Edging cutters	Light purple	530
Embossing dies	Light yellow	440

Table of Tempers to Which Tools Should be Drawn, Arranged
Alphabetically—Continued.

Tool.	Color.	Deg. of Tem. F.
F		
Flat drills for brass	Brown yellow	500
Flat drills for steel and iron	Straw yellow	460
Firmer chisels	Dark purple	550
Framing chisels	Dark purple	550
G		
Gimlets	Dark purple	550
Gauges	Brown yellow	500
H		
Hammer faces	Very pale yellow	430
Hand plane irons	Brown yellow	500
Half-round bits	Straw yellow	460
Hack saws	Dark purple	550
Hand tools	Light yellow	440
Hand springs	Purple blue	529 to 531
Hammers and drop dies	Spotted red-brown	510
I		
Ivory-cutting tools	Very pale yellow	430
Inserted saw teeth	Straw yellow	460
J		
Jaw pieces	Purple blue	529 to 531
L		
Leather-cutting dies	Straw yellow	460
Lathe tools for brass	Very light yellow	420
Large cutting dies	Straw yellow	460
Large forging dies for press	Dark yellow	490
M		
Moulding and planing tools	Dark purple	550
Milling cutters	Straw yellow	460
Milling cutters for brass	Very light yellow	420
N		
Needles	Dark purple	550
P		
Press dies for brass	Light purple	530
Press dies for cold-rolled stock	Brown yellow	500
Press dies for sheet steel	Straw yellow	460
Press dies for leather	Straw yellow	460
Press dies for paper	Dark blue	570
Penknives	Straw yellow	460

*Table of Tempers to Which Tools Should be Drawn, Arranged
Alphabetically—Continued.*

Tool.	Color.	Deg. of Tem. F.
Planer tools for iron	Straw yellow	460
Planer tools for steel	Very pale yellow	430
Parts subject to shock	Very dark blue	601
Paper cutters	Very pale yellow	430

R

Rock drills	Straw yellow	460
Reamers	Straw yellow	460

S

Shell reamers	Brown yellow	500
Screw-cutting dies	Straw yellow	460
Scrapers for brass	Very pale yellow	430
Steel-engraving tools	Very pale yellow	430
Scrapers	Very light yellow	420
Slight turning tools	Very pale yellow	430
Screw drivers	Dark purple	550
Springs	Dark purple	550
Saws for wood	Dark blue	570
Saws for bone and ivory	Dark purple	550
Stone-cutting tools	Brown yellow	500
Small milling cutters	Straw yellow	460
Shear blades	Dark yellow	490
Springs	Very dark blue	601

T

Twist drills	Brown yellow	500
Taps	Straw yellow	460
Threading dies for brass	Light yellow	440
Truing blocks	Straw yellow	460
Tools for wood, to be filed	Purple blue	529 to 531
Tools for wood, not to be filed	Spotted red-brown	510

W.

Wood-engraving tools	Very pale yellow	430
Wood-boring cutters	Brown yellow	500
Wire-drawing dies	Straw yellow	460

Table of Suitable Temperatures for—   Deg. F.

Annealing steel	900 to 1,300
Annealing malleable iron (furnace iron)	1,100 to 1,400
Annealing malleable iron (cupola iron)	1,500 to 1,700
Annealing glass (initial temperature)	950
Working glass	1,200 to 1,475
Melting glass (into fluid)	2,200
Hardening tool steel	1,200 to 1,400

Table of Suitable Temperatures for—   Deg. F.

Casehardening iron and soft steel..................1,300 to 1,500
Core ovens in foundries................................... 350
Drying kilns for wood.................................... 300
Baking white enamel..................................... 150
Baking red and green enamel........................... 250
Baking black enamel..................................... 300
Vulcanizing rubber...................................... 295

Table of Temper Colors of Steel.   Deg. F.

Faint yellow... 430
Straw color 460
Dark straw.. 470
Brown yellow... 500
Purple 530
Blue 550
Full blue ...:.. 560
Polish blue... 580
Dark blue... 600
Pale blue... 610
Blue tinged with green.................................. 630
Bright red in dark...................................... 725
Red hot in twilight..................................... 884
Red visible by day...................................... 1,077

CHAPTER VI.

The Use of Machine Steel for Press Tools.

For a large number of purposes, particularly in the line of sheet metal working, machinery steel tools, if properly hardened, will answer as well and sometimes better than tool steel ones, and if the following process is used to harden such tools they will be found to give the best of results and may be used with success for cutting the different metals. In order that the parts or tools may do their work and last long, they must be hardened very deep and come out with a fine compact grain. For dies which are to be used for punching regular shaped blanks from light soft stock, machine steel casehardened tools will give excellent satisfaction, as they are far cheaper to make and will last as long as though made of tool steel.

Outfit for Fine Grain Casehardening.

To do this work properly the following outfit is necessary: A good hardening oven, a number of hardening boxes, a good supply of raw bone, granulated, the same amount of granulated charcoal, some hydro-carbonated bone and the same amount of charred leather. A tank large enough to hold a good supply of water, a small tank so arranged as to allow of heating to any desired temperature, and a bath of raw linseed oil, and the outfit will be complete.

Packing and Heating the Work.

Pack and heat the work as you would for regular casehardening, and leave it in the oven to cool. When perfectly cool heat the pieces in hot lead and quench the same as tool steel. If the pieces are small they should be re-packed in the hardening box with granulated charcoal and heated. When packing in charcoal do not mix with any kind of bone or any other carbonizing matter; such substances open the grain, and the object of the second heat is to close the grain. The hardening heat should be as low as possible, and the hardened pieces will come out close in grain, with a hard, tough surface all over, while the center remains soft and the piece will be stronger than if made of tool steel.

Casehardening Cutting Tools.

When machine steel tools are to be used for cutting they should be packed for the first heat in a mixture composed of equal parts of charcoal and charred leather, finely granulated. The use of charred leather gives a much tougher effect to the steel than bone, as the leather is almost free from phosphorus, while bone is not, and as phosphorus makes steel brittle the substance which contains the least amount of it should be used. Tools which are to be used for bending and forming may be packed in bone, which will carbonize them as required. When using either bone or leather an equal amount of granulated charcoal mixed with it will prevent the kernels of bone and leather from adhering and forming a solid mass when hot, and as charcoal is an excellent conductor the pieces packed within the hardening box will be heated quicker than if no charcoal were used.

How to Caseharden, Color and Anneal with Granulated Raw Bone.

In order to attain good and satisfactory results in casehardening by the use of granulated raw bone, as well as to color and anneal properly with it, the treatment of the steel must be in accordance with the use to which it is subsequently to be put. In the following we give special directions for casehardening, coloring and annealing machine steel by the use of Hubbard's granulated raw bone. The matter was kindly furnished to the author by the manufacturers of the bone, Rogers & Hubbard Company, Middletown, Conn., who have gone to much trouble and expense in order to discover the best methods for casehardening, coloring and annealing under different conditions, and for parts used for special purposes.

To Caseharden Without Colors.

Pack the work to be hardened in a cast-iron box. The box should be of suitable size; use a box about 4 inches deep, 4 inches wide and 8 inches long. Put a layer of granulated raw bone in the bottom, then a layer of work to be hardened, and so on until the box is full within 1½ inches of the top. This space may be filled with old bone that has been used. Put on the cover and lid and lute with clay. In packing, be sure to keep the work at least one-half an inch from the sides and ends of the box. Heat to a good cherry red from three to four hours, according to the depth of hardening desired. Dump the whole contents in clear, cool, soft water. Delicate pieces should be dumped in oil. For larger work use a larger box and keep in longer.

Hardening Extra Heavy Work.

To harden pieces 4 inches and upward in diameter the work should be packed in clear raw bone, No. 1 or No. 2, surrounded by at least 1½ to 2 inches of the "one," and heated to an orange, or almost white heat, for 18 hours, and then plunged into cold running water, salt water preferred. If the piece does not harden hard enough at one operation, it should be repacked and heated again, the same as the first time, and plunged into cold water as before. Great care should be taken in heating these pieces. After the heat is up to the required temperature, it should be kept so until the piece is ready to be plunged into the water.

Hardening Drawbridge Disc and Similar Work.

Large flat pieces require especial care and treatment. For hardening pieces or discs 2 feet in diameter and 4 inches thick, put four or five inches No. 1 granulated raw bone in bottom of packing box. On this bed lay work to be hardened flat side down, pack at least four inches of granulated raw bone around the diameter and on top. If you have any charred leather, a thin layer added next to the work may prevent scaling, but it is not a necessity. After packing, cover the box with an iron cover and lute with clay. Heat to a bright cherry red and hold at this heat for eight or ten hours. These large flat pieces have a tendency to warp a little, but this can be reduced to a minimum by being careful not to heat above a good cherry, and by dipping the pieces edgewise into a large body of cold water, which has a steady stream running into it, or some other way of keeping the water agitated.

In hardening large flat pieces, there are four essential points —plenty of bone; even, steady, bright cherry heat; dip edgewise; large body of water that is kept agitated.

Hardening Five-inch Thrust Bearing Rings.

If made from ordinary soft machinery steel with about .10 per cent or .15 per cent of carbon, it would be necessary to pack them in No. 2 granulated raw bone and heat twelve hours to a good bright cherry red, then re-pack and heat nine hours again to a good bright cherry red.   Dip in salt water singly (do not dump). We would advise using a cast-iron box 11 inches long, 7 inches deep, 6 inches wide, covered with an iron cover that will fit inside. Lute around the edge with clay.   Such a box will hold ten rings.

To Harden Rods or Rolls, Leaving Tenons Soft for Riveting.

Finish the pieces to the required diameter, leaving a little extra length for trimming, but do not turn the tenons on the end or ends. Pack and heat the pieces as usual, but do not dump.   Allow the work to remain in the boxes until all heat has passed off the same as the annealing.   On being taken from the boxes the pieces are thoroughly annealed with the outer surface carbonized to a greater or less depth, according to the time they were in the furnace.   After turning the tenon heat the piece to a cherry and plunge into cold water the same as to harden tool steel.   On removing from the bath the work will be found to be extremely hard wherever the outer surface has not been removed since carbonizing, but wherever this surface has been removed, as in turning the tenon, the softness of the original stock has been removed. If the stock is required in rods for tenon, screw or similar machines, cut in pieces as long as your furnace and pots will take, carbonize and anneal as described above.   The finished work from these rods upon coming from the machines is ready to harden, leaving such portions soft as have been turned or cut after carbonizing.

The principle of this method is that only carbonized portions will harden when heated and chilled and as the carbon enters but a short distance the carbonized surface may readily be removed, thus leaving the original stock, which will not harden, exposed to the action of the fire and water.   The principle may be adapted to a great variety of uses where hardness and softness are required on the same piece.

When it is not practical to remove any of the stock in order to remove the carbonized surface, the parts desired soft may be protected by covering them with a coating of fire-clay, thus preventing the carbonizing of the stock at these particular points, with the result that when plunged in the cold bath they will remain soft.

To Caseharden Malleable Iron.

If malleable iron is thoroughly malleable it should be treated exactly the same as any wrought iron. If it is only half annealed, as some of it is, then there are no directions to give in regard to it. Sometimes it will take a light casehardening, sometimes it will harden half way through, other times all the way through, according to the condition it is in. If it is thoroughly decarbonized, as it could be, then it is just about the same as a piece of iron.

In order to obtain the best results it is necessary to employ a furnace that gives and maintains a good uniform heat.

To Use the Old Bone.

After dumping the pots, separate the bone from the work and dry it thoroughly; it will then be coal black. This can be used again by adding new granulated raw bone, about one part new to two of the old. Place upon your bench a box each of the granulated raw bone and the bone black; one is white, the other black; a mixture will make a gray. For very small work, screws, etc., use a dark gray, i. e., two or three parts bone black and one of the raw bone. For very large work use white or raw bone; a little proportion of raw bone and burned bone to be used for different sizes of work. The different shades of gray make an easy and reliable guide after having once become familiar with them.

Pameacha raw bone may be used in exactly the same way. The shades of the color are not as true a guide, however, as the pameacha raw bone is quite dark-colored itself.

Constant burning will finally turn the bone white; it is then valueless for casehardening.

Bone and Charcoal.

The following is recommended by a reliable party as a practical and economical method of using granulated raw bone: For ordinary iron work, such as set or cap screws, etc., use one part granulated raw bone to three parts pulverized charcoal, thoroughly mixed; in this we pack our work in iron pots, then sprinkle a little charcoal dust on the top. In casehardening Bessemer steel or fine small drawn work we diminish the quantity of bone somewhat. Pameacha raw bone may be used in the place of the granulated raw bone, but the proportion of charcoal should be somewhat diminished.

Using the Tell-Tale.

Parties who have had but little experience in casehardening may find the "tell-tale" a help to them. The tell-tale consists of a piece of round iron, as near the size of the work to be hardened as possible, that reaches down into the center of the pot, extending up through the cover about high enough for the tongs. The hole in the cover should be just large enough to allow the pin or tell-tale to slip out readily. When you think the work has been in long enough, remove the tell-tale with the tongs without disturbing the pot, and plunge it immediately into cold water. There may be one or more tell-tales in the cover, as desired. If the tell-tale shows the work to be hardened to sufficient depth, dump as instructed, otherwise leave in longer, and test as before.

To Obtain Colors with Granulated Raw Bone.

This process not only gives the finest colors and mottling, but it casehardens the work at the same time.

Preparation of the Work.

To obtain bright colors, the work must be nicely polished and perfectly clean; poorly finished, greasy work will not take bright colors. A clean, brightly polished surface is necessary for the finest work.

To Char the Bone.

To produce the colors the granulated raw bone must be thoroughly charred. This can be easily and cheaply done by putting it into iron boxes about 9 x 9 x 36 inches, covering tightly and placing it in the furnace at night, after the work has been withdrawn. The remnant of fire and heat of the retort is sufficient to char the bone during the night. If, however, there is much fire left, it must be partially deadened, as the object is to simply char the bone without burning it. If the smaller boxes are used, they must be watched and taken out when "one" is charred. If there is sufficient oven room this can be arranged so as to be done during the day.

To Pack the Work.

Pack the work in a cast-iron box of suitable size for the work; for screws or similar work ¼ to ¾ inch, use box 4 inches deep, 4 inches wide and 8 inches long. Put a layer of charred bone in the bottom, then a layer of the work to be hardened and colored, and so on until the box is filled to within 1½ inches of the top;

fill this space with charred bone, put on the cover and lute with clay. In packing, be sure and keep the work at least ½ inch from the sides and ends of the box, and do not let any two pieces of the work come in contact.

The Heat.

Place the boxes in the furnace and bring to a cherry red, and hold at this heat two to four hours. To get nice colors, the heat must be held uniform; if too hot, there will be no color. A good nice cherry red must be maintained from the time the boxes are placed in the furnace until they are ready to dump. With very small work this time may be reduced somewhat; with heavy work it may be increased. A little practice will be necessary to determine this point.

In order to obtain the best results it is necessary to employ a furnace that gives and maintains a good uniform heat.

The Bath.

While good colors can be obtained in rather hard water, yet soft water will give much better results. The bath should be arranged as follows: Bring your water pipe up through the bottom of the barrel reaching about half way to the top; make the outlet about six inches from the bottom of the barrel; into your supply pipe connect a pipe from an air pump so that the air and water will mix in the pipe and come into the barrel together. When dumping, have a running stream of water and air floating into the barrel. Hang a sieve under the surface of the water in which to dump the work. While the air pump is not absolutely necessary, yet its use gives more satisfactory results. Running water is necessary if large lots are to be dumped, as the water must be kept cold. Small lots may be dumped into the bath of still water.

To Dump the Work.

When the work is ready to dump, draw the boxes from the furnace, hold them close to the surface of the water over the sieve and dump, turning over the box quickly. This operation requires the nicest care, in order that the air may not strike the iron before it reaches the water. If the air strikes the iron, it assumes a black or blue-black streaked color.

Cleaning the Work.

Separate the work from the bone and **boil** out in clean water.

Dry in sawdust and oil over slightly, which will bring out the color and keep it from tarnishing.

Colors from a Light Straw to a Deep Blue.

Caseharden the articles as instructed, then roll them in a tumbling barrel of some sort, until they are brought to a proper finish.   After they are thoroughly polished, place them in a cylinder and tumble them over a regular gas blaze until drawn to a desired color, then plunge in cold water, dry in sawdust and oil slightly to avoid tarnishing.   By using a regular gas blaze, and noting the exact time required, the process can be timed exactly to produce any color desired from the light straw to a deep blue. If preferred, you can put the pieces in a wire cylinder where you can see the color, and revolve over a slow fire.   The fire must be free from gas or the pieces will be stained.

Directions for Annealing with Granulated Raw Bone.

Pack the work to be annealed about the same as for casehardening, but it is not necessary to keep the pieces separate, using the bone that has been burned a number of times until it is almost white.   Place in the oven and heat until it is heated through to a cherry red.

Cooling.

As soon as the work has reached the required heat stop the blast, and if the oven is not required for further use, let the boxes remain in the furnace and cool down with the fire.   Upon removing the boxes from the oven cover them with warm ashes, old burned bone or air-slacked lime, so as to retain the heat as long as possible.   Do not remove the work from the boxes until all heat has passed off.   The more gradual the cooling the better the results.

To Anneal Low Carbon Steel Bars.

For bars 6½ inches in diameter use 9-inch iron pipe for packing box, other sizes in proportion.   Pack the steel in a mixture of half charcoal and half bone that has been used once or twice. This proportion does not tend to recarbonize more than five (5) per cent, and in all cases it is sufficient to maintain the amount of carbon originally in the steel.   Great care must be taken in heating steel for annealing, heating it only to the same degree of heat that you would for casehardening, i. e., a good cherry red.   Heavy bars 6 inches to 7 inches in diameter should be placed in the furnace in the morning and left in until the next morning, but no draft should be allowed on during the night. Upon removing the box from the furnace cover them with warm ashes, old burned bone or air-slacked lime, so as to retain the heat as long as possible. Do not remove the steel from the boxes until all heat has passed off.

Smaller bars are treated in exactly the same way except the length of time required for heating; this diminishes as the size of the bar is reduced.

To Anneal Iron Castings.

To anneal small or thin iron castings, pack them in a cast-iron pot with a mixture of bright cast-iron turnings or filings and pulverized charcoal, half each; have a layer of the mixture between the castings; it will help to keep them from warping and heat them more uniformly. Place the pots in the oven and bring to a good bright cherry red, then let them cool off. If it is necessary that they be very soft, hold them at a bright red for two or three hours.

It is absolutely necessary that the castings be left in the pots to cool off.

In order to obtain the best results it is necessary to employ a furnace that gives and maintains a good uniform heat.

Casehardening with Cyanide of Potassium.

The casehardening of machinery steel with cyanide of potassium can be accomplished in a number of different ways. The most common method of casehardening with cyanide is to heat the article to almost a white heat and soak it into a cake of the cyanide, then reheat and plunge into water. This method, however, is a very poor one except for special jobs or a few small articles.

A highly satisfactory method of casehardening with cyanide can be attained by melting the cyanide in an iron pot, and dipping the heated articles into it. To use this method for hardening small articles a cast-iron pot will answer, while for large pieces or ones with delicate portions, which are to be merely colored, a mild steel pot will be necessary.

In Fig. 78 a cheaply made pot of the second kind is shown. It can be made of flat mild steel from two pieces of ¼-inch to ⅜-inch thick, which should be bent to the shape shown and riveted and welded together. With a pot of this kind soft steel pieces may be heated in the cyanide, and when dipped properly in water will show up with colors equally as clear as those possible to attain by packing and heating in bone and leather. One decided advantage of this process, for certain articles, is that delicate parts will not spring out of shape, as no hardness is produced in them, which is a decided advantage in a large variety of work which is required to be colored, but not hard.

When the articles are desired to be hard the cast-iron pot may be used, although care will be necessary in order to prevent excessive warping in any but very small pieces.

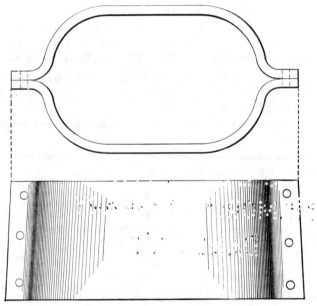

FIG. 78.--SHEET STEEL POT FOR CYANIDE HARDENING.

A strange thing about this process is that the first time a new steel pot is used the work heated in it will come through as hard as if a cast-iron pot was used. To overcome this, heat a new pot once before doing any work. Where a great deal of this work is done a hard coal-burning furnace should be built with a lid of cast-iron on the top or roof, in which a hole about the shape of the pot has been cored. In hardening or coloring by this method be sure that the articles are perfectly dry before putting them into the cyanide. If there is any moisture or dampness in the grain the cyanide will fly like hot lead.

Accurate Sectional Casehardening.

The accurate sectional casehardening of special machinery steel parts may be accomplished by a special process so that the hard and soft surfaces may be controlled with absolute accuracy.

Take the article or part, of which sections only are desired to be hardened, and coat the surfaces requiring hardening with black Japan enamel, having first thoroughly cleaned the surfaces to be afterward enameled, and after they are perfectly dry have the work plated with copper, being sure that the Japan coating has not been eaten away by any cleaning fluids.

After plating, the piece must be carbonized, which ordinarily requires from three to four hours at a bright red heat in bone dust. At this heat the pores of the metal open and freely absorb the carbon. After the heating period has expired remove the box and allow the article to cool slowly in the bone dust. When the part is cold remove from the bone, heat to a red in an open fire and quench in cold water.

The fracture of a piece of metal treated as described above will present a fine velvety appearance, this being brought about through the second heating. If the part is quenched after the first heating or working process, a coarse grain will be the crude result.

Upon testing the properly heated piece with a file, it will be found that the plated surfaces are soft and the Japanned ones hard. This result comes about through the copper plating preventing the absorption of carbon during the roasting process and the Japan burning off and allowing the opposite to occur, allowing the carbon to penetrate to a depth of 1-16 inch. By repeating the process the hardened surface will deepen and the structure of the metal will not deteriorate.

To Produce Fine Grained Hardened Machine Steel Parts.

The reason why machinery steel has not been adopted and used extensively in place of expensive tool steel is that very few mechanics are able to harden it so as to produce a fine grain. When it is considered that machine steel would replace to advantage many tool steel parts if the process for producing a fine grain was generally known the value of the method is obvious.

All steel parts which are subjected to pressure, wear, or concussion are required to have a strong close-grained backing in order to stand up well when in use.   Tool steel has this fine grain, while machine steel in its natural condition has not, and when case-hardened, by the ordinary process, the grain becomes even coarser through the pores opening during the heating process when the carbon is absorbed; the higher the heat to which such parts are brought the coarser the grain.

To harden machine steel parts and articles so as to produce a grain equal to that of high-grade tool steel proceed as directed in this chapter under heading, "The Use of Machine Steel for Press Tools." The process will answer for all parts and articles which can be made from mild steel which will be subjected to strain, wear or pressure, such as cutting dies for thin stock, form-ing and bending dies, cams, plug, ring, and snap gages; bicycle, sewing and typewriting machine parts, spindles, and a variety of other parts which will suggest themselves to the reader.

Casehardening Ends of Steel Rails.

A process for casehardening the ends of track rails, which or-dinarily are of comparatively short endurance because of the greater wear to which they are subjected, has been invented by M. E. Coyan, of the Carnegie Steel Company's Works, at Home-stead, Pa. The process obviates loss of service, now quite general, in having to remove tracks with battered ends, while the inter-mediate portions are yet sound. The description of the process as given in the "Railway Review" is given below:

In operation the rails are passed through the finishing rolls and are sawed off and placed on a horizontal table. Located at each end of the table and near one side is a spray designed to deposit a casehardening solution on the ends of the hot rails as they enter the table. The rails are kept moving across the table the same as in usual treatment, the casehardening material burning and soaking into the ends until the rail runs in contact with water sprays, located just opposite the casehardening sprays, and so constructed as to extend half the length of the table. The ends coming in contact remain in the bath until they reach the opposite side of the table, where they pass from out of the bath and are carried away for straightening.

Very Deep Casehardening.

When small mild steel articles are required to be hardened very deep, put the parts into a crucible and add enough cyanide of potash to cover them when melted. Cover the crucible and heat as required, then remove parts and quench into a cold water bath. Parts treated in this manner will harden very deep.

To Caseharden Small Iron Parts.

Put into an iron pot, or crucible, 1 part prussiate of potash and 10 parts of common salt, fuse together, and put articles in. Allow the parts to remain in the liquid for 30 minutes, after which quench in cold water, and a good caseharden will result.

To Caseharden with Charcoal.

To caseharden with charcoal, the articles finished, but not polished, should be put into an iron pot, and covered with an animal or vegetable charcoal, and brought to a red heat, when they will cement. The heat should be kept up for a period varying with the size and description of the articles worked upon.

Moxon's Method of Casehardening.

Cow's horn or hoof is to be baked or thoroughly dried and pulverized in order that more may be packed in the box with the articles to be worked upon. Bones reduced to dust will answer the same purpose. To this add an equal quantity of bay salt; mix then with this stale chamber-lye, cover the iron with this mixture, and bed it in the same as loam, or inclose it in an iron box. Lay it on the hearth to dry and harden, and then put into the fire. Heat the mass until a blood red heat—no higher—appears, and then remove the iron and quench in cold water.

A Casehardening Mixture for Iron.

A good casehardening mixture for iron is composed of equal parts prussiate of potash, sal-ammoniac and saltpeter; add 4½ ounces more of sal-ammoniac and 7 gallons of water. Heat the iron red hot and soak it in the composition.

A Casehardening Paste.

To caseharden iron parts quickly and satisfactorily, make a paste with a concentrated solution of loam and prussiate of potash. Coat the parts to be hardened with the paste and heat them to a bright red, after which allow them to cool to a dull red and then quench in a cold water bath.

Casehardening Polished Parts.

To caseharden mild steel or iron parts which have been previously finished and polished, heat them to a bright red in a closed fire and wipe them with prussiate of potash. When the prussiate appears to decompose and dissipate, quench the article or part in cold water. When the process has been conducted properly the surface of the parts will be well hardened to a depth sufficient to resist a file. This process will be found to be a great improvement over the ordinary method as the application of the prussiate allows of casehardening a part, or a number of parts, of the articles and still leave the remaining sections soft.

Casehardening as it Should be Understood.

In order to caseharden successfully it is not *merely* necessary to follow the directions herein given. The *principles* must be understood and retained in order that the operation shall be accomplished in a manner fitting special requirements. In the first place the operation of casehardening consists first and foremost of giving a surface to steel or iron that will be capable of receiving a great external hardness, while the interior remains soft and in its natural tough state. Thus the part will be capable of withstanding wear, strain and concussion when in use. Second, the above mentioned results can only be accomplished satisfactorily by packing and heating the parts in close vessels filled with animal carbon.

The following being kept in mind, no difficulty will be experienced in performing casehardening operations successfully: Pack in a good animal carbon, make the box air-tight by luting with clay, place in fire and keep at a red heat for a length of time sufficient to allow of hardening to the depth desired—a half hour of heat will allow of hardening 1-32 inch deep, an hour 1-16 inch, two hours ⅛ inch, and so forth, the longer the heating period the greater the depth to which the pieces will be hardened. After the heating period has elapsed the parts may be taken from the box and quenched in cold water, or better still, they may be reheated to a cherry red and then quenched. When cool, remove from the water and dry thoroughly, to prevent rusting, by riddling them in a sieve with dry sawdust. To keep delicate articles from blistering during the heating process, dip them into a powder of burnt bones, leather, or some other coaly animal matter.

CHAPTER VII.

Hardening Milling Cutters in the Open Fire.

For the hardening of milling cutters and tools of a similar nature, water or brine is mostly used, the liquid being kept in a tank with an exhaust pipe and a supply pipe connected with it. Solutions are used to some extent and good results are obtained. On the whole, however, success in hardening such tools depends principally upon the man who does the heating and quenching.

To harden a milling machine cutter in the open fire, have a large, high charcoal fire and bury the cutter well in it and use only enough blast to heat the work to the required temperature, being careful to get the heat uniform throughout. If the cutter has not been annealed after roughing and drilling the hole through it, remove it from the fire when red hot and allow it to cool off slowly until a black appears. It can then be again placed in the fire, slowly brought to the required heat, plunged into the bath of tepid water or brine and worked around well until it stops "singing." At this point it should be removed and instantly plunged in the oil bath and left there until it is cool, when the strain should be removed by holding over the fire until it is warm enough to snap when touched by a drop of water. It can then be laid aside and the temper drawn at leisure. In hardening punch press dies they can be treated the same; if there are any screw holes for stripper or guide screws they should be filled with fire clay, graphite or asbestos. Much depends on an even, uniform heat; uneven heat causes more cutters and dies to crack than high heat. Steel should never be given any more heat than is necessary for the operation desired.

Hardening Large Milling Cutters.

Large, plain or former milling cutters, say over $3\frac{1}{2}$ inches in diameter and 4 inches long, to harden should be packed in a mixture of equal quantities of granulated charred leather and charcoal, taking care not to have any part of the mill within, say, 2 inches of the box at any point. Keep it in the furnace for 4 to $4\frac{1}{2}$ hours after the box is heated through to a low red; remove the box from

FIG. 79.—A COLLECTION OF PLAIN MILLING CUTTERS.

FIG. 80.—TYPES OF MILLING CUTTERS.

the furnace at the expiration of the time and quench the cutter in
a bath of raw linseed oil, twirling it around rapidly in the oil so as

FIG. 81.—SPECIAL FORM-
ING CUTTER.

FIG. 82.—DOUBLE FACE
MILL.

to cause the oil to come in contact with the teeth.   Allow the
cutter to remain in the oil until cold.   A formed mill with heavy
teeth does not need to have the temper drawn.   Mills with

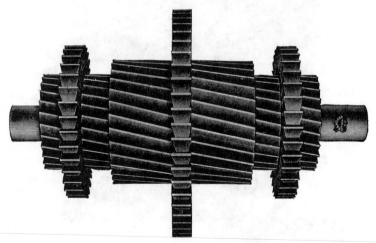

FIG. 83.—GANG OF STRAIGHT-FACED MILLING CUTTERS.

teeth cut in the ordinary manner should be run quite as long, and
may be drawn for ordinary work to a light straw color, or if drawn

in a kettle gaging the heat by a thermometer to 425 or 430 degrees Fahr.

We have seen a large number of milling cutters and similar tools treated by this method and have never known one to be lost by cracking. In years of experience with this method we have had but a few pieces crack.

Hardening and Tempering Milling Cutters in Water and Oil.

A rapid and highly satisfactory method for hardening and tempering milling cutters is by the combined oil and water method.

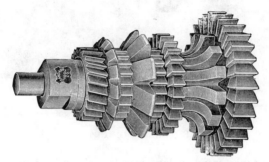

FIG. 84.—GANG OF MILLING CUTTERS FOR MACHINING A WIDE-FORMED SURFACE.

When only a small quantity of such tools are required, this method will be found superior to the ordinary hardening and tempering method.

The method is as follows; The cutter to be hardened is heated

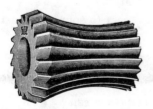 

FIG. 85.—FORMED FACE MILL.   FIG. 86.—SHELL END MILL.

to a proper uniform temperature, quenched into a cold-water bath and left there long enough to harden the outside only, but not enough to cool the steel clear through. It is then taken from the water as quickly as possible and plunged into lard oil and held there until the outside is almost cold.   The tool is then taken from the oil and the "temper" immediately drawn by allowing the heat remaining in the core of the tool to draw the teeth; this may be aided to some extent by holding the tool in the flame of the forge or furnace.   The reheating should be continued until the oil commences to smoke.   To insure an even temper it is best to then

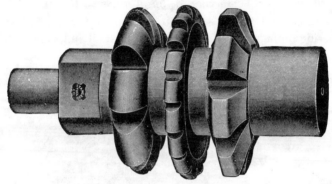

FIG. 87.—GANG OF CUTTERS.

plunge the tool for an instant into the oil and again heat, doing this several times until the smoke rises evenly from all over the tool.   This second plunge into the oil tends to cool off any fine points that might become overheated, while the tool is not left in the oil long enough to cool off the thicker parts, thus insuring a more uniform and evener heat than would be the case if the tool were heated all at once.

Advantages of the Method.

The above-described method may seem to some to be a more

FIG.·88.—SPECIAL MILLING CUTTER.

tedious one than that ordinarily used, but as the time saved is considerable, and the results, particularly in experienced hands, are much more reliable, it should be adopted where good milling cutters are required.

The ordinary method of tempering tool-steel milling cutters is to heat the cutter to the proper temperature and then cool it "dead cold" in water, brine, or solution. When cold it is removed from the bath and the teeth are polished. Then the cutter is "drawn" to the proper color by heating from some external means, such as over a red-hot piece of iron or a low fire, or in oil or sand bath.

The polishing for tempering takes considerable time, as it must be pretty well done in order to allow the temper colors to show up

FIG. 89.—SPECIAL END MILL.　　　　FIG. 90.—TAPER MILL.

properly. Then, again, the steel is "dead cold" and will require considerable heat to raise it to the proper temperature to give the desired temper. All the heat that goes into the steel must go through the cutting edges, leaving them as soft as, if not softer, than the body of the tool, when they should be the hardest part of the tool. By the other methods the results are different, as the

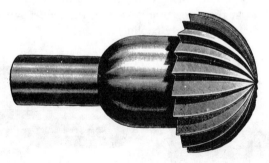

FIG. 91.—FORMED BUTT MILL.

teeth, or cutting edges, which are, of course, the parts that are wanted hard, are hard; while the central part or core of the tool is comparatively soft, which is in all cases a desirable condition.

When milling cutters are hardened in water they often crack, cracking taking place not, as might be imagined, when the hot steel is first plunged into the water, but about that time the central part is becoming real cold, as the outside cutting edges are properly hardened while the inside is yet comparatively hot; and when the inside cools and contracts while the outside remains rigid, the cracking takes place. **The slower** the tool is cooled, the longer the time in which the central metal has a chance to "adjust" itself to molecular changes, and consequently there is less liability of crack-

FIG. 92.—FORMED BUTT MILL.   FIG. 93.

ing. For this reason hardening in oil is not as liable to crack tools, but for the same reason the tools are not as hard.

By the oil and water method the outside is hardened in water and the inside in oil, thus giving the cutting edges the required hardness and at the same time lessening the tendency of cracking or warping by more slowly cooling the inside.

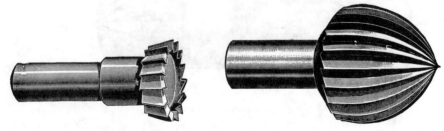

FIG. 94.—ANGLE END MILL.   FIG. 95.—FORMED BUTT MILL.

A good way to decide upon the proper instant at which to draw the tool from the water, when hardening the outside, is to put the hand in the water near the tool, and as soon as the water ceases to boil on the surface of the steel, the tool should be removed from the water and plunged into the oil bath.

The object of this cooling first in water and then in oil is this: The outside of the tool is wanted very hard; the inside somewhat softer. The faster the heat is abstracted from the heated tool, the harder it becomes; so by first plunging it into the water the cutting edges are given the desired degree of hardness, and as soon as they are hardened, the tool, with the central part still hot, is

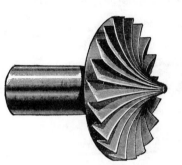 

FIG. 96.—SPECIAL FORMED BUTT MILL.   FIG. 97.—END MILLS.

plunged into oil; and as the oil does not abstract the heat as fast as the water, the steel has more time to adjust itself to molecular motion and there is less tendency to crack. Again, the oil left on the outside of the tool serves as an indicator for determining the temperature at which to reheat the steel to give the proper temper. As the tool is not completely cooled in the oil, very little

FIG. 98.—SPECIAL MILL.

external heat is required to draw it. In fact, the drawing of the temper really begins immediately upon removing the tool from the water bath.

Lard oil is the best to use in tempering in this way, and it has been found that the oil commences to show a very faint smoke at about the same temperature as a light straw; the proper temper may be considered as reached when the smoke is seen coming from all parts of the tool.

Tools tempered in this way will prove to be harder and yet tougher than those tempered according to the ordinary method. Milling cutters from ¼ inch in diameter up have been tempered

FIG. 99.—SPECIAL MILL.

FIG. 100.—ANGULAR END MILL.

in this way, as well as taps of various kinds and sizes; reamers and other like tools so tempered have always been very satisfactory.

Hardening V-Shaped Milling Cutters.

The following directions for hardening V-shaped milling cut-

FIG. 101.—DOUBLE SLOTTING END MILL.

FIG. 103.—FACING MILL.

FIG. 102.—END MILL.

ters for milling tool steel if followed out will be the means of securing satisfactory results.

Heat the cutters in a gas furnace, open fire or in a hot lead bath. Not so much depends on the *means* used for heating as upon *how hot* and whether uniformly heated; and as to lead sticking to the work, if it is used, there should be little trouble if pure lead is used with plenty of broken charcoal on top to prevent oxidation; but if there is still trouble it can be avoided by coating the article with salt before putting into the lead-heating bath. This is easily done by warming the work up to a blue and dipping in a strong solution of salt and water.

In hardening, the cutters may be cooled in cold water or brine, temperature depending on the character of cutter, whether very

FIG. 104.—HOLLOW MILLS.

delicate or not. With some heavy cutters it might be ice cold, while in the case of very thin, delicate cutters it would be better to have the bath up to blood heat or even higher; it is simply a question of preventing cracking.

Remove the cutters from the cooling bath as soon as the teeth have cooled sufficiently to harden, and instantly immerse them in oil to remain there, if convenient, until cold.

How to Harden Hollow Mills.

When hollow mills are to be hardened, care should be taken when heating not to heat very much above the teeth, as it is not necessary for the back to be hard. When the proper heat has been attained, the mill should be inverted and hardened in the bath with the teeth up, and it should be worked up and down rapidly in the bath in order to force the contents into the hole.

Better results are always attained if this method of dipping is adopted with pieces having holes running part way through them, as then the steam can escape and the water can enter the hole; whereas, if dipped with the opening down, steam which generates rises in the hole, and as there is more steam than the hole can contain, it escapes from the bottom and blows the water from the teeth, not allowing them to harden properly. Vapors generated in the bath are a source of annoyance often overlooked by inexperienced hardeners, and often cause a great deal of trouble.

Milling Cutters.

Milling cutters may be classified in four distinct types. The first and probably the most common form is known as the axial, Fig. 105, in which the surface cut is parallel to the axis of the cutter. This cutter has teeth on its periphery only; these may be

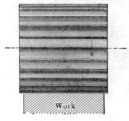

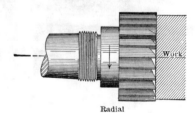

FIG. 105.—AXIAL TYPE   FIG. 106.—RADIAL TYPE OF
OF MILLING CUTTER.   MILLING CUTTER.

straight or spiral teeth. Cutters of this character, made in appropriate widths, are used very much for milling broad, flat surfaces and for cutting keyways in shafts. For deep cuts, or for slitting metal, they are made of large diameter and thin. These are called metal-slitting saws, and are ground hollow on the sides for clearance.

The second class of cutters is known as the radial, Fig. 106, in which the surface cut is perpendicular to the axis of the cutter. These cutters are called radial because their teeth are used in a plane parallel to the radii of the cutter. End mills, face mills, butt cutters, etc., are all tools in this class.

The third class of cutters is the angular, Fig. 107, in which the surface cut is neither parallel nor perpendicular to the axis of the cutter, but is at some angle with this axis. Frequently cutters are made with two different angular cutting edges, in which case the angle is marked on each side.

The fourth class of cutters is the formed cutter, as shown in

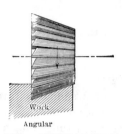

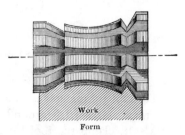

FIG. 107.—ANGULAR TYPE OF MILLING CUTTER.

FIG. 108.—FORMED TYPE OF MILLING CUTTER.

Fig. 108. The cutting edge of this class is of an irregular outline. When properly backed off, these cutters can be ground and retain their original form. Gear cutters, tools for grooving taps, etc., are all classed as form cutters.

Among the numerous engravings in this book will be found

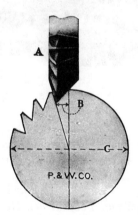

FIG. 109.—CUTTER FOR SPIRAL MILLS. INCLUSIVE ANGLE B IS 52°; 40° ON ONE SIDE, 12° ON OTHER.

illustrations of a large number of cutters which are used on milling machines. In most cases it is advisable to use a cutter of small diameter rather than of large diameter. Cutters from $1\frac{1}{2}$ to 2 inches in diameter are the most economical for general milling.

CHAPTER VIII.

HARDENING, TEMPERING AND STRAIGHTENING ALL KINDS OF SMALL TOOLS.

Hardening Ring Gages.

To harden ring gages and other tools of a similar nature so that they will harden around the hole and leave the remaining parts soft, clamp the tool between flange-ended tubes and allow

FIG. 110.—U. S. STANDARD THREAD GAGES, EXTERNAL AND INTERNAL.

a stream of water or brine to circulate through them. By this method the walls will harden out as far as the inner edges of the clamping flanges.

Dipping Small Tools When Hardening.

When small tools such as penknife blades, razor, lancet, chisel, gage-bit, place spoke sheaves, three and four square files, round and flat files, iron-shaving knives are to be hardened great care must be taken to dip them into the quenching bath endwise or perpendicularly. By doing this they will come out straight, while, on the contrary, if they are slanted while dipping, there will be a tendency to warp.

Dipping Half-Round Reamers When Hardening.

When hardening half-round reamers or any other tools that are solid and half-round, enter them at an angle of about twenty degrees with the surface of the bath. This will tend to keep them straight. In a half-round tool there is once and a half as much surface in the half-round portion to be hardened as on the flat side, and as in hardening the contraction of the steel is equal, according to the surface, it is necessary to dip the half-round side at the angle mentioned. As the half-round portion has a greater percentage of contraction than the flat side, the unequal contraction will draw the reamer to one side and warp it.

Dipping Fluted Reamers When Hardening.

When hardening fluted reamers, dip them perpendicularly to a short distance beyond the fluting, that is to say, about half an inch, and withdraw and return them a number of times. This will harden all the lips, and prevent them from cracking off at

FIG. 111.—COUNTERSINK.   FIG. 112.—SMALL ANGLE MILL.

the water's edge, which is usually the case when a piece of steel is dipped into a certain depth and allowed to cool without moving. A number of different tools are often broken off at the ends in this way, without anyone knowing what caused them to crack.

Straightening Tools Which Have Warped in Hardening.

When a piece of steel which has been hardened and tempered is found to have sprung, it may be straightened as follows: Heat it slightly, not enough to draw the temper, and it may be straightened on the anvil with a hammer. This cannot be done when the piece is dead cold. It is best, however, to straighten a piece whenever possible between the centers of a lathe, or on a block of wood with a mallet. Warm, the steel will yield readily to the blows of the mallet, but cold, it will break like glass.

A sword blade which has warped in hardening may be hammered flat; too much hammering, however, will cause the blade to lose its elasticity. When this occurs it may be returned to its elastic state again without re-hardening by heating slowly to a spring temper. This method may be adopted to advantage for other kinds of work also.

Hardening Very Thin Tools so as to Prevent Warping.

A good way to harden very thin tools so as to insure against their warping is to heat them carefully and stick them into a raw potato. Then remove and temper as desired over a gas flame.

Warping of Long Tools in Hardening.

Trouble with the warping or the twisting of long tools, such as taps and reamers, in hardening and tempering, can be avoided

FIG. 113.—INSERTED CUTTER PIPE TAP.

if care is taken. If, in hardening, one can so manage as to retain a soft center in the article there will be, or need be, but little difficulty in overcoming the warp. This will at least be found true in large tools which have a larger proportion of soft core than those of smaller cross-section. With these last, and in fact, in all, care must be taken to lower the tool perfectly square into the quenching bath, so that the heat will be absorbed equally from all sides. This desirable tendency will be increased if the tool is lowered in the center of the bath.

If the above is true about the hardening bath, it is equally so of the heating bath, where melted lead or other liquids are used for heating. One thing must be remembered, and that is that there will be no use in taking the trouble to cool a tool equally if it has been heated unequally. For this reason, tools should be immersed squarely and centrally into the heating-bath, and turned around. The turning process will also contribute to good results in quenching.

Temperature "Tell-Tales" for Use in Heating Steel.

In order to show just how hot steel is that is being annealed in a muffle or box, supply some one-fourth inch rods, which may be pulled out from time to time to test the temperature.

Working Steel for Tools.

In forging steel for tools great care must be taken to hammer all sides alike. The careless and unequal hammering of steel when forging is responsible for a great deal of bad work in hardening. Another thing, steel, when being forged, should be heated as hot as it will stand until finishing, and should then be hammered until almost black-hot. This treatment will set the grain of the steel finer, and give a tool a better edge when finished. The reason for heating the steel to a bright red heat while forging is simply because it makes the steel tougher when hardened and softer when annealed; while, on the contrary, when steel is worked at a low red heat, the continued shocks of the hammer will so harden it as to make it almost impossible to anneal it, and at the same time render it too brittle, when hardened, for general use.

Hardening Small Saws.

To harden small saws such as are used for screw head slotting, etc., heat on a flat surface and clamp between two thick cast-iron plates, which should be perfectly level and coated with a heavy grease.

Hardening Cutter-Bits.

Cutter-bits such as are used in lathe tool holders should be hardened regularly when soft at the lower ends. When too soft to use they should be laid aside until a sufficient number of them are at hand to be hardened. They can then be heated by putting them into a box and heating them to a dull red, and the end of each stuck into a perforated iron pan, the bottom of which should be covered with just a sufficient depth of water to harden them up as far as desired. The tools may then be ground and put with the new cutters. Do not let high-grade steel such as should be used for cutter-bits get into the smith's fire.

Hardening Mixture for General Smith Work.

Salt, 2 ounces; copperas, 1½ ounces; sal-ammoniac, 1½ ounces; saltpeter, 1½ ounces; sal-soda, 1½ ounces, and black oxide magnesia, 8 ounces. The last two ingredients should be added after the others are mixed together. Before mixing the ingredients, pulverize them separately, and then mix well and dry before using. Use like yellow prussiate of potash and plunge in water.

Tempering Flat Drills for Hard Stock.

Procure good high degree steel and heat to a cherry red, and hammer until nearly cold, forming the end into the requisite flattened shape, then heat it again to a cherry red, and plunge it into a lump of resin or into quicksilver. A solution of cyanide of potassium in rain water is sometimes used for the tempering plunge-bath, but it will not give the result that quicksilver or resin will.

To Temper Gravers.

Gravers may be tempered in the same way as drills; or the red-hot tool may be pressed into a piece of lead in which a hole about half an inch deep has been cut to receive the graver; the lead melting around the article will give it an excellent temper.

To Temper Old Files.

Grind out the cuttings on one side of the file until a bright surface is obtained; then moisten the surface with a little oil, and place the file on a piece of red-hot plate with the bright side upward. In about a minute the bright surface will begin to turn yellow, and when the yellow has deepened to about the color of straw, plunge in cold water.

Hardening and Tempering Small Taps, Knives, Springs, Etc.

Secure a piece of pipe of sufficient diameter and length to accommodate the piece, and heat one end, flatten together on the anvil, and weld so it will not leak. Fill the pipe with lead and set it up in the fire. When the lead has melted, immerse the tool and let it remain until the lead is red-hot. Then quench in a salt water bath and when cool remove it. To temper the tool, heat a large piece of iron in the forge to a red heat. Grease the tool all over with tallow. Remove the iron from the forge and lay on the anvil. Hold the tool over hot iron by means of tongs or pliers, turning it all the time until the desired color is obtained and then drop it into linseed oil. A good and uniform temper should result.

Tempering Small Spiral Springs.

To temper small spiral springs heat to a cherry red in a charcoal fire, and harden in oil. To temper, blaze off the oil three times; the same as for small flat springs.

To Draw Small Steel Parts to a Blue.

Fill a cast-iron box with sand and heat it red hot. Then put the article, which has been first highly polished, into the sand and when the right color appears remove and quench in oil.

Small steel parts of guns, typewriters, sewing machines, etc., may be blued cheaply and well in a solution of ten parts saltpeter and black oxide of manganese, heated in an iron pot to the point where sawdust thrown on it will flash.

Small pieces may be strung on wires in considerable quantities and dipped in solution, a minute or two being sufficient time ordinarily, although of course this will vary with the thickness of the pieces. The blue produced by this process is what is called Government Blue and is not quite equal to the English Blue, which is secured with hot charcoal and whiting, as all gunmakers will understand, but it will answer very well and is very much cheaper.

If springs are to be blued, they may be hardened and polished and the bluing process will draw them to the proper temper at the same time, and the temper will be very uniform.

It will be well to bore some holes in the solution before placing on the fire to heat, for if a vent is not provided there will be a commotion.

CHAPTER IX.

The Hardening and Tempering of Press Tools.

Of the hardening and tempering of dies and all manner of
press tools too much cannot be written, as upon the results of
this part of their construction depends the efficiency of the tools.
For heating dies a gas furnace is preferable, but when this is not
at hand a good clean charcoal fire will do.

For hardening large dies it is indispensable to have a large
tank which should be arranged in such a manner as to insure the
rapid cooling of the steel. A tank of this kind can be arranged
by fixing two or three rods across the inside about 12 inches
below the surface of the water, and a pipe let into the tank in
such a manner as to allow of a circulation of a stream of water

FIG. 114.—COMBINATION DIES, WITH HARDENED AND GROUND TOOL
STEEL WORKING PARTS SOLID-FORGED TO WROUGHT-IRON PLATES.

from the bottom upward. When the die is to be quenched the
water should be turned on and kept running until the steel has
cooled. When a good circulation of water is kept up in the tank
there will not be any soft spots in the die after hardening.

It is often necessary to construct dies from forgings of
wrought iron and tool steel, and, as the dies when finished are
required to be hardened, it is necessary there should be a good
weld between the two parts. To accomplish this result, when
welding mix mild steel chips, from which all of the oil has been

removed, with the borax and there will be no difficulty in producing a clean weld and one which will not buckle or separate in hardening.

Hard or Soft Punches and Dies.

At times, when tools are required for sheet-metal working, it is hard to determine whether a punch and die should be hardened, or whether one of them should be left soft, and if so, which one? The stock to be worked and the nature of the work have to be considered when deciding this matter. Some classes of work will be accomplished in the best manner by using a soft punch and a hard die; others when a hard punch and a soft die are

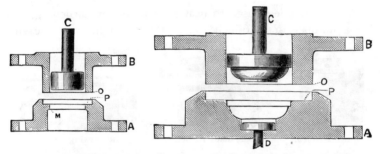

FIG. 115.—"PUSH-THROUGH" CUTTING AND DRAWING DIE.

FIG. 116.—SOLID BOTTOM CUTTING AND DRAWING DIE.

used, while in a majority of cases the best results will be obtained by using a punch and die that are both hard. For punching or shearing heavy metals both die and punch should be hard, while for all metals which are soft and not over 1-16 inch thick, a soft punch and a hard die will be found to work well. By leaving one of the dies soft it will be easy to produce clean blanks during the life of the tools, as when the punch and die become dull it will only be necessary to grind the hard one, upset the soft one and shear it into the die.

Hardening and Tempering Drop Dies.

If there is one class of tools the hardening of which is less generally understood than others, it is the class used for drop press work. When dies of this class are to be hardened special care is necessary. Instead of plunging the whole die into the quenching bath (when heated properly) set it in an inclined position and direct a strong stream of cold water onto the face of the die. By having the stream strong the whole die face will be covered, and the contraction of the metal at the surface will be equal. Allow the water to strike the die until the bath ceases to boil, and then gradually diminish the stream and allow the die to cool slowly. By placing the die in the inclined position when hardening, the water will run off the face and thereby the bottom will remain soft and hot while the die portion proper will be hard, which is always a desirable condition in dies of this kind. At the same time the temper can be drawn by the heat remaining in the base of the die. When the colors appear turn the water on until cool.

When a muffle is used to heat steel parts for hardening, provide a number of 3-16-inch rods. Put them in with the steel

Redrawing Punch.   Inside Blank Holder.   Redrawing Die.

FIG., 117.—REDRAWING DIE WITH INSIDE BLANK HOLDER.

and remove one from time to time during the heating process to test the temperature.

To anneal white or hard iron die parts so that they may be machined with ease, put the parts into an iron box and pack around them a mixture composed of equal parts of common sand, fine steel turnings and steel scale from the rolling mills. Wet the mixture with the solution of sal-ammoniac, after which place the box in a furnace and heat to a white heat. Keep the heat for five or six hours, and then allow the box to cool slowly. When cool remove the castings and they will be found to be malleable enough to allow of cutting them. The packing of the mixture mentioned above and the wetting of it with the solution contributes to the annealing, and allows of the castings or parts coming through the process free from scale and lumps.

How to Harden Large Ring Dies.

To harden large ring dies, which are to be ground after hardening, and which are required to be very hard about the center of the hole and the walls, they should be heated in large iron boxes as follows: Put a layer of fine powdered charcoal about 2 inches deep in the bottom of the box and place the die on it. Fill the die and then cover it to a depth of about ¾ inch with a mixture of 4 parts powdered charcoal to 1 part of charred leather, then put a loose cover on the box and place in the furnace. After heating about three hours or more, according to the size of the die, the metal will be at a red heat. It should then be allowed to remain at a low heat for about an hour, which will insure its heating uniformly throughout. The heat should then be increased until the die comes to a full red heat; it is then ready to be quenched.

Remove the box from the furnace, and with two pair of tongs, and a man at opposite sides, if the die is too large for one man to handle, draw the die from the box, clean, and quench squarely

Drawing Punch.　　Blank Holder and　　　　　　Die.
　　　　　　　　　Cutting Punch.

FIG. 118.—DOUBLE-ACTION CUTTING AND DRAWING DIE.

into the water, working up and down until the red has entirely disappeared, then let it lie still until cool. When cool remove the die from the water and heat, to remove the strain and chill of hardening, until drops of water sprinkled on it will steam. Then lay it aside in an even temperature where it will cool off slowly.

When large ring dies are hardened in the manner described above there need be no fear that they will warp, crack or shrink excessively or unevenly.

Hardening a Long Punch so as to Prevent Warping.

Often, after carefully hardening a long punch, it will be

found to have warped during the process—often to such an extent as to make it useless. There is a way by which this tendency of the steel may be eliminated altogether—at least the warp will be so little as to not affect the working qualities of the tool. To eliminate the possibility of warping lower the steel, when at the proper heat, squarely into the tub, lowering it as far as possible in the center of the water. When this is done the heat will be absorbed equally from all sides and the tendency to warp excessively will have been overcome.

Steel for Small Punches.

When small punches are required to punch heavy stock or to operate at high speeds, never use drill rod or Stubs steel, for the reason that such steel is of the finest high carbon variety and will crystallize rapidly under concussion. In place of such material use one of the low grades of steel; one which in order to harden it will be necessary to heat to white heat, and the punches will last much longer than if made from the best grades of steel.

For small punches which are required to pierce thin, soft stock, or to operate at a slow speed, get the best grades of steel procurable, as for such uses the finer the grade the better results which will be obtained.

Hardening a Blanking Die.

In order to harden a blanking die properly great care should be taken; first in the heating of the steel, and second in the

Drawing Punch.   Blank Holder.   Die.

FIG. 119.—WASH-BASIN DRAWING DIE.

quenching. In all shops where dies or other tools which require hardening are constructed, a gas furnace or "muffle" should be used for heating, but when a "muffle" is not handy charcoal should be used. After a good clean fire has been built, all screw and dowel holes in the die should be plugged with fire clay or asbestos. By taking these precautions the tendency of the steel to crack around the holes is, as far as possible, eliminated. We now heat the die to an even cherry red, so that the entire plate will be the same temperature; then remove it from the fire and dip it endwise into the water (which should first be warmed slightly to take the chill out), being careful to dip down straight, and not to move it or shake it around as that would increase the possibility of the die warping, or shrinking excessively. After removing the die from the water it should be immediately warmed. Now grind the face of the die; heat a thick piece of cast-iron red hot, and place the die upon it; it can then be drawn evenly to any temper desired. By taking a piece of oil waste and wiping the face of the die as it is heating, the different colors will show up clear. When the color denoting the temper required appears, remove the die and allow it to cool off slowly.

Cracks in Dies—Their Cause.

When a piece of tool steel in itself of no great commercial value is worked out and finished into an intricate die the labor cost amounting to a large sum, the steel is, of course, very valuable; and if cracks show after the hardening process, or the die is spoiled, it means a great loss to the establishment.

Now in the first place, although we are apt to usually confound cracks with hardening, very often the trouble can be traced to the preceding operations of annealing, forging and finishing. Of course there is a large number of dies spoiled through carelessness or inexperience in hardening, but still we believe there is as great an amount spoiled through imperfect preceding operations or through the operator not being familiar with the nature of the steel.

A die may be carefully heated to give the proper temperature throughout, and may be quenched in the bath in the most approved manner, but if it is not "slightly warmed" after removing it from the hardening bath, it is liable to crack. This reheating may be done in a number of ways. The best way is to hold the die over the fire until it is heated to a temperature sufficient to cause a few drops of water to steam when sprinkled on it. The heat will not be sufficient to make any of the temper colors appear.

The author has been connected with one establishment where thousands of dies were made every year, and every die was reheated after hardening, in the following manner: A large tank provided with a perforated tray with means for raising and lowering it was used. The tank was filled with water to within two inches of the top and a steam pipe was connected with it. Then the water was kept at the boiling point, and the die directly after hardening was placed upon the tray which was then lowered into the bath.

We have known dies to crack while being in the forge when the blaze touched the die portion proper. This being brought about by a sudden heat and then a cold blast of air causing the steel to expand and then suddenly contract again, at a certain point, and as the consequent expansion and contraction in the die does not extend over the entire surface, the charge was local and cracks resulted.

A die made from a blank cut from a bar and machined and worked out without annealing is liable to crack when subjected to the hardening process, particularly if the blank is for a blanking die of odd shape, as shown in Fig. 120. If annealed bar steel is used the necessity of reannealing is also imperative as the first annealing does not eliminate the liability of cracking.

When it is not possible to anneal the die blank before finishing to size, the next best thing to do is to heat the die uniformly throughout to a red heat, then remove it from the fire and allow it to cool until black. It may then be reheated to the proper temperature and hardened. In a forming die the bulky portion has a tendency to contract away from the small portions, which being frail, harden first and do not alter their shape, while the bulky portion continues to contract unevenly, after the thin portion becomes ridged, and cracks are apt to appear when the tool is removed from the quenching. By heating the die to a high or red heat and then allowing it to cool to a black before the hardening heat this uneven contraction is to a certain extent provided for.

In hardening a die the quenching of it so that the frailest portion enters the bath first and hardens before the thickest portion, will most invariably cause cracks to appear, as unequal contraction takes place and the heavy portion contracting the most, changes shape in attempting to draw with it the frailer portions.

Another cause of cracks in dies is the use of improper means for grinding. When a die is ground on a machine on which no provision is made for water cooling, or where a fine wheel is used, cracks often result, coming about through the steel being unevenly heated during the grinding. Thus, by using a coarse wheel with a free water supply this disagreeable possibility will be eliminated.

Hardening the Walls of a Round Die.

Often, in die work, it is desired that the walls of a drawing die, for instance, or some other part, such as the inside of a

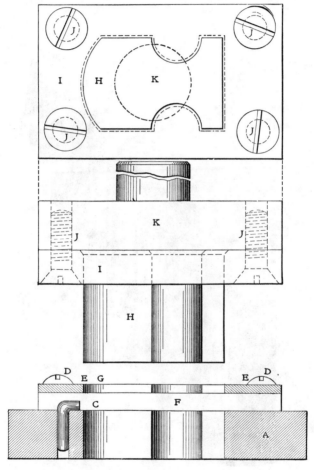

FIG. 120.—BLANKING DIE.

hollow punch, should be hard and the remaining portion of the piece soft. This may be accomplished by proceeding as follows: Clamp the die or punch, as the case may be, between flanges on the ends of tubes, being sure to have the steel at the proper heat. Then allow a stream of cold water or brine to circulate through the tube and the metal will harden in depth as far as the inside edges of the flanges while the remaining portion will remain soft.

Reannealing a Punch or Die Blank.

Sometimes a piece of steel, which is to be used for a punch

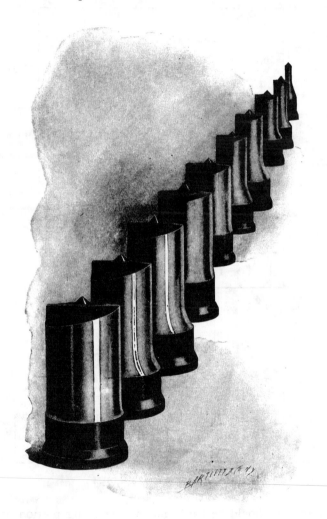

FIG. 121.—PUNCHES FOR PERFORATING HEAVY STOCK.

or die, upon starting to machine it, proves hard, although it has been annealed. When this is the case, never try to finish it before reannealing it; instead, rough it down, clean out the centers, if there are to be any, and anneal it over again. The time required to reanneal the piece of steel will be more than made up in the machining of it.

Warping of Long Punches in Hardening.

Often after carefully hardening a long punch it will be found to have warped during the process, often to such a degree as to make it useless. There is a way to avoid this altogether, or at least the warp will be so slight as to not affect the efficiency of the tool. To insure against warping, plunge the steel, when at the proper heat, squarely into the bath, lowering as far as possible into the center of the liquid. When this is done the heat will be absorbed equally from all sides and the tendency to warp excessively will have been eliminated.

Hardening Very Small Punches.

When a large number of very small piercing punches are to be hardened they should be packed in closed iron boxes and the box heated. When all the parts have reached the proper heat they should be entered into a bath of either oil or water, as the nature of the work may require, through a funnel. This will insure the entering of the parts vertically and prevent warping. Another way by which small punches may be heated uniform is by means of the lead bath. Keep the lead at the proper heat and cover the top with powdered charcoal and coke.

Tempering Small Punches.

Almost all large die shops in which any amount of hardening and tempering are done have discarded the method of tempering by colors, and have adopted the more reliable method of doing it in oil, gaging the heat by thermometer. A kettle containing the oil is placed on the fire and heated to the right temperature for the degree of temper desired in the work. The hardened parts are then thrown into the liquid until drawn. By this method there is no possibility of overdrawing, as it is impossible for the parts to become hotter than the oil. When tempering punches in this manner it is not necessary to brighten them before the operation, and where a lot of such work is done, it will be accomplished much cheaper than if the old method were used; besides the most satisfactory results will be attained.

Hardening Fluids for Dies.

We have heard a great deal about hardening fluids, for which it is claimed dies can be hardened better than in water or in brine. Such fluids are composed chiefly of acids and will rot the steel, and we should advise keeping away from them, as where it is not possible to harden die steel in clear water or strong brine, the steel is useless and should be dispensed with. When quenching the heated steel dip down straight and don't shake it about, but after keeping it stationary for a few seconds, move it around slowly, keeping it vertical all the time. When the die or punch is of an intricate shape, about three inches of oil on the top of the water will toughen it and contribute to helping the steel retain its shape while hardening, and prevent it from warping or cracking during the process. Lastly, immediately after hardening and before grinding, the steel should be placed on the fire and slightly warmed, to take the chill and contraction strain out and not laid aside for a while, as we have seen dies that were laid aside after hardening (that were intact) after a few hours, show cracks.

Hardening Thick Round Dies.

Often round dies, which are very thick in proportion to their diameter, contract excessively in the center during the hardening process, often to such a degree as to make them unfit for use. To overcome this tendency have an arrangement by which a stream of water may be forced through the hole without wetting the outside; allowing the water to only come in contact with the inside of the die. By doing this the walls of the die will be hard while the outside will remain soft, as when the temper is drawn the hole will remain straight and true. In shops where grinding facilities are not at hand this method will work excellently. If possible use strong brine for the hardening fluid.

Hardening Poor Die Steel.

Quite frequently in making dies we run across a piece of steel which after working will not respond satisfactorily to the usual hardening process. When this occurs prepare a solution composed of two handfuls of common salt and one ounce of corrosive sublimate to about six quarts of water and when the steel has reached a good red heat plunge into the bath. The corrosive sublimate gives toughness to the steel and the salt hardens. This solution is *deadly* poison; exercise care in using it.

Tempering a Combination Cutting and Drawing Punch.

After the face of the punch has been slightly sheared, and the edges of the drawing die slightly rounded and highly polished, the punch is hardened and then drawn by laying it alternately on each of its four sides on a hot plate, tempering the cutting edges to a dark blue and leaving the inside or drawing die portion as hard as possible. When finishing the blanking portion of the punch, care has to be taken to do it so that the drawing portion will be perfectly central.

Hardening and Tempering a Split Gang Punch.

The best way to harden and temper a split gang punch is by the following method: It should first be heated and hardened in clear oil, dipping it from the back, and thus preventing—as far as possible—the legs from crawling in toward each other because of the channel between them. By dipping from the back this will be overcome, as by the time the cutting face is immersed the back will be hard and set. It should then be polished and tempered by drawing from the back to a dark blue to within ¼ inch of the cutting faces and quenched when those portions are a dark straw color.

Hardening and Tempering Large "Blanking" or "Cutting" Dies.

Large "blanking" or "cutting" dies of the type shown in Figs. 122 to 127 require considerable skill and experience to harden and temper correctly. They should be carefully heated and then quenched into a large tank of water and when cold warmed on the fire to take the chill and strain out.

Cutting dies consist of an upper "male" die or "punch," and the lower, or "female" die. They may be made in almost any size and shape for cutting out flat blanks in tin, iron, steel, aluminium, brass, copper, zinc, silver, paper, leather, cloth, etc. Ordinarily, the lower die is hardened and tempered to a degree best suited for the work, while the punch is left comparatively soft, so that it can be "hammered" up when worn. Sometimes, as in the case of playing-card dies, it is preferable to reverse this and make the punch hard, leaving the die soft. Circumstances determine whether any or how much "shear" should be given to the cutting edge. For ordinary work in tin, brass, etc., a moderate amount of shear is desirable. These dies require to be made with the utmost care, of materials specially adapted for the purpose, and by experienced and skillful workmen. Ordinarily, the steel cutting rings are welded to wrought-iron plates, after which they

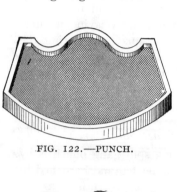

FIG. 122.—PUNCH.

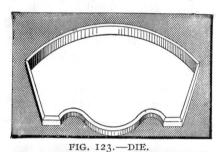

FIG. 123.—DIE.

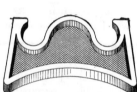

FIG. 124.—PUNCH.

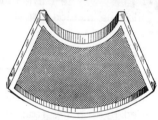

FIG. 126.—PUNCH.

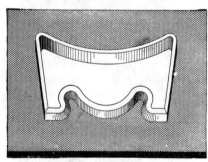

FIG. 125.—DIE.

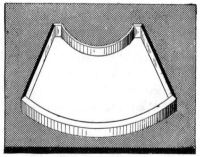

FIG. 127.—DIE.

are hardened, carefully tempered and ground on special machinery. In some cases it is preferable to fasten the steel dies in cast-iron chucks or die-beds by means of keys or screws. This applies more particularly to small dies. For cutting thick iron, steel, brass, and other heavy metals both the die and punch should be hard and provided with strippers.

CHAPTER X.

Welding Heats.

In the welding of steel to steel or steel to iron without injuring the quality of the material, the process involved is one in which great care, judgment and skill are necessary, particularly in dealing with the degrees of heat. Because of its greater flexibility the welding heat of steel should be lower than that of iron and thus the more flexible the steel the harder it is to weld. Mild steel can be welded much more easily than high carbon or tool steel. Ordinary cast steel such as double shear steel, containing as it does a smaller proportion of carbon than "tool steel," may be easily welded, as its texture, which is very fibrous, is partly restored through hammering or rolling. Thus for all edge tools for wood this steel will give good results as it will carry a very keen cutting edge.

A Good Welding Flux for Steel.

A good flux for welding steel is sal-ammoniac and borax. The borax of commerce as sold by chemists is composed of a very large proportion of water, and in order to use this, it should be put into an iron or other suitable vessel and boiled over the fire until all the water is expelled, after which it should be ground to a powder before it is used. When it is desired to mix sal-ammoniac with borax the proportions are about 16 parts borax to 1 of sal-ammoniac. In heating a piece of steel for forging it should be placed in the center of a close hollow fire and the wind put on very sparingly, so as to allow the mass to heat equally through and through. If, on the other hand, it is put into the fire and the blast turned on full the outside of the metal will become red hot before the center; therefore the expansion of the outside away from the center will cause internal strains, which will not be visible until the tool is hardened, and then the hardener will be blamed.

Heating Steel for Forging.

A great many smiths say that steel should not be heated above a cherry red; but the best way is to heat the steel to as high a heat as it will stand with safety, and draw down under steam hammer, if there is one handy. Then the whole mass will draw down in the center as well as around the outside, where, on the contrary, by heating to a cherry red one would only be drawing the outside away from the center, which would show fracture when cooled. We do not mean that the steel should be heated high when the tool is nearly finished; then the cherry red heat will do, being also careful not to hammer after the red has disappeared, but put it back in the fire and heat as evenly as possible. Sulphur is the greatest enemy to contend with in the heating of steel. To fully illustrate the effects, heat a piece of cast steel almost to the scintillating heat, and by holding a piece of sulphur against it, it will drop to the floor, the same as a piece of sealing wax would do with a match. A man who is forging and welding iron should never be asked by the foreman to dress a tool, as that man is blind to the colors of steel which reveal themselves in the tempering.

Steel for Tools Which Require to be Forged.

In purchasing tool steel for the various kinds of tools that are used in metal working it is best to state to the steel maker what kind of tools the steel is required for, as steel that is suitable for cold chisels is too low in carbon for lathe and planer tools. High carbon steel cools far quicker under the blows of the hammer than low, and the scales that fall from the former are small and silky while the latter are large.

The amount of working one will get out of a tool which has been properly forged, tempered and ground is unlimited. It is a bad economy to buy cheap steel for tools of any kind. It only results in worry and vexation and poor work.

High Grade Steel Forgings in America.

Few people are probably aware of the important change that has taken place in machine construction in this country as a direct result of the improvements in the manufacture and forging of crucible cast steel, first introduced by the Bethlehem Steel Company, Pennsylvania, U. S. A. Without these improvements the large power units now used in the electric generating stations would have been impossible, for no forgings could have been obtained that would have been able to sustain the tremendous strains of such machinery. When steel forgings were first employed for large work they were generally considered inferior to iron forgings, because, as is well known, steel is not as easily forged as iron and is more easily injured in the process, while the methods used in forging were not adapted to the requirements of the new material. The improvements in the manufacture of steel came through the efforts of the government to obtain steel suitable for large guns and the parts of marine engines, which, according to law, had to be built in this country, and of American material. A brief history of how the change of iron forgings to high-grade steel forgings came about, and the manner in which hollow shafts are forged, is given in the following and is taken from a paper by Mr. H. F. J. Porter, read before the 1902 meeting of the Engine Builders' Association:

At the time George H. Corliss built his Centennial engine he had his own smithshop in which his shafts and other engine forgings were built up out of small fagots of wrought iron. This was about the time when steel began to encroach upon iron in the trades. Before this time wrought iron was a staple article in the market. The quality of this material, coming from the rolling mills, was very high, demands for high grades having brought about methods of precaution which supplied the trades with extra refined iron, very free from slag and dirt. The small forges sparsely scattered about the country were equipped with hammers of ten tons falling weight with top steam, sufficient in capacity to thoroughly work and weld together the few fagots of iron which were required to build up the moderate sized forgings which the various industries demanded. When steel made its appearance, however, manufacturers generally began to appreciate the fact that the market contained a new material, stronger and more reliable than wrought iron. Desirous of having the forged parts of their mechanisms smaller and lighter, they attempted at once to obtain forgings made of this metal. Had the forgers made proper efforts to acquaint themselves with the nature of the new material before attempting to supply it, a very different condition of affairs would have come about, not only in the forging industry, but in the steel industry at large, which resulted from the first unintelligent effort at production. At the meeting of the Railway Master Mechanics and Master Car Builders, at Old Point Comfort, in 1899, Captain (now Admiral) Robley D. Evans delivered an address in which he said:

"In 1882 I had the good fortune to be a member of what is known as the first advisory board for rebuilding the navy. It was an awfully hot summer, and fifteen of us, rather impatient in spirit, got together in Washington, presided over by Admiral John Rodgers. When we looked the field over, we found that we had no navy at all; we were hopelessly behind the age, and it seemed hardly worth while to rebuild our navy. I shall never forget as long as I live the trouble I caused in that small convention by proposing that we should build steel ships. I was the original steel man, and when I proposed that all ships in future should be built of steel, Admiral Rodgers adjourned the board for three weeks to prevent a fight."

Now the animus referred to by Admiral Evans was induced by the fact that forgings which were being supplied at this time were of just such a type as might be expected to be produced by men who had not acquainted themselves with the requirements of the new material. While some were excellent in every way, others were different in strength, or contained concealed cavities and were unreliable in general. The supplies of material running so irregular in quality reflected unfavorably upon the steel industry at large and developed a prejudice against steel generally, from which it has scarcely recovered in the minds of many users of forgings, even at the present day. It was fortunate for the country that the advisory board referred to contained as stalwart a champion of steel as Admiral Evans, for after they had visited the various ordnance works abroad and had seen steel worked properly, they returned home and recommended to the Secretary of the Navy Mr. Tracy, that by all means the new navy should be built of this metal, and as there were no properly equipped steel forges in this country, one would have to be built to furnish the necessary armor, guns and engine forgings required in the construction of modern naval war vessels. Meanwhile, this board had overcome, through the good offices of its secretary, the personal objections heretofore existing on the part of Sir Joseph Whitworth to the use of his special steel casting and forging processes elsewhere than in his own works, which were considered foremost in the manufacturing of ordnance. Without entering into the details which accompanied the immediate establishment in this country of the great ordnance works of the

Bethlehem Steel Company, it is sufficient to say that in their equipment not only were special appliances in use in this English works duplicated, but their size was doubled. A contract was also entered into at the same time by which the great works of Schneider & Co., of Le Creusot, France, which stood first among the makers of armor plate, were also duplicated at the Bethlehem plant. Thus there arose in this country a forging plant at once larger and superior to any in the world.

During the years this plant was being erected there were many engineers who, appreciating the superior advantages of steel forgings when properly produced over those made of wrought iron, systematically sent abroad for their steel forgings. It was not until 1889 that the country obtained its first high-grade steel commercial forgings from the Bethlehem works. These had been gladly specified by the engineers above mentioned who were impatiently waiting to get their steel forgings nearer home than in Europe. Machine and tool builders of this country were thus made acquainted for the first time with steel forgings intelligently produced. There are to this day many users of steel forgings who, not having carefully investigated the methods considered necessary to produce them, think that a steel forging is made by merely hammering a rolled steel billet to the form required; and such as order their forgings without specifying more definitely the grade called for by the special service to which the forging is to be submitted may get a forging of that type. The forging industry has grown from the blacksmith shop, a once familiar adjunct to an engine works, and has become a specialty; and a modern steel forge is not now thought complete unless it melts its own raw material and converts it into the finished product under the supervision of chemists, metallurgists, physicists and microscopists.

How Hollow Shafts Are Forged.

There are two ways of making a forging hollow. The ordinary way of getting rid of the center of a forging is simply to bore it out. After boring, it is tempered and thus the strength is restored which was taken away with the material which was in the center.

Another way of getting rid of the center of large forgings is to forge them hollow. A person who has not considered the subject carefully would naturally think that the first thing to do in making a hollow forging would be to cast a hollow ingot. It has been mentioned that there were various defects which occur in ingots, the most serious of which are "segregation" and "piping" and that it is in the center and upper portion where those defects occur. If an ingot were to be cast hollow, a solid core of fire-brick or similar material would replace the center metal, and instead of one on the outside there would be two cooling surfaces, one on the outside and one around the core, and the position of the last cooling would be transferred to an annular ring, midway between these surfaces, where the "piping" and "segregation" would collect. This would not be satisfactory, because the metal there is what must be depended upon for the strength of the hollow forging. It is necessary, therefore, to collect the "piping" and "segregation" in the center and the top, where the metal has been added to the original ingot for the purpose.

Then having cut off the top and bored out the center, the "piping" and "segregation" are entirely eliminated and what is left is as sound and homogeneous a piece of steel as can be obtained.

After the hole has been bored in the ingot, the next process is to re-heat it, and, as before explained, this process is not as de-licate a one as if the ingot were solid. The heat affects the center equally with the interior and they expand together and the danger of cracking is not incurred. When the ingot is re-heated a steel mandrel is put through its hollow center, and sub-jecting the two to hydraulic pressure the metal is forced down and out over the mandrel. Thus an internal anvil is practically inserted into the forging and there is, therefore, really much less than one-half the amount of metal to work on than if the piece were solid.

When the work of shaping is completed the forging is re-heated to the proper temperature and then either annealed in the usual manner or plunged into a tempering bath of oil or brine, to set the fine grain permanently that has been established by the re-heating. A mild annealing follows to relieve any surface or other strains that may have been occasioned by the rapid cooling.

Hollow forgings oil-tempered and annealed are considered the best grade of forgings made, and any forgings made otherwise, although they may be suitable for the service to which they may be applied, cannot be looked upon in any other manner than as of an inferior grade.

That steel forgings of such high grade were being manufactured for commercial purposes in this country was first brought to the attention of manufacturers generally at the World's Fair in Chicago. Here were exhibited stationary engine forgings which compared favorably with those sent over by European forges. The Ferris wheel shaft, 45 feet long and 32 inches outside diameter, with a 16-inch hole through it, represented the largest made up to that time. The soliciting of orders for such forgings, however, at once aroused the latent prejudice still existing against steel forgings, and the prices demanded being somewhat in excess of those which wrought iron or ordinary steel forgings could be obtained for, prevented at first the very rapid introduction of this product into the commercial field.

Difficulties Encountered in Introducing High-Grade Forgings.

It hardly seemed necessary to explain to an engineer or any one authorized to purchase, and therefore presumably competent, that if he wanted material to sustain severe usage in the nature of alternating stresses, to which all forgings are subjected, he should select a material possessing a very high elastic limit. And yet it was not unusual to find that those very people preferred to use wrought iron for their engine crosshead and crank pins and shafts in preference to steel, because, as they said, "steel being crystalline is brittle and snaps off suddenly under such services as that under consideration, while iron having fiber, is tougher and yields before breaking." Most of these men know better, but had not given the subject sufficient thought, or they would have perceived that their statements were not consistent. They said that the steel connecting rods they had tried had broken off short without any warning, while rods made of wrought iron had simply bent up, and after having been straightened out were replaced as good as new.

These people did not stop to think that a steel rod that broke off had done so at its ultimate strength, or under a stress of from 80,000 to 90,000 pounds per square inch, whereas the iron rod which had doubled up had done so at its yielding point of 25,000 to 30,000 pounds per square inch. In other words, their engines with wrought iron rods were failing all over the country under loads about one-third what they were standing up to when supplied with steel rods, yet the men were blaming the steel for helping them out of their troubles.

Then again they complained that steel shafts and crank pins heated up, while wrought iron ran cool. When it was proved to them that laboratory experiments showed the coefficient of friction of these metals to be the same, and that any difference in heating was caused by local circumstances, such as poor lubrication, excessive pressure, etc., they said they did not care for laboratory experiments. They had an engine in one place with a steel shaft that never would run cool, while another with a wrought-iron shaft had never given any trouble, and they were passing judgment on their own experience. Persistent exposure of these fallacies gradually brought about a change in sentiment.

"Cold Crystallization" Does Not Occur.

It took a long time to persuade people who had seen broken forgings which showed a coarse crystalline section that the metal had not crystallized from shock or vibration in service, but had been forged in such a manner that the crystallized condition of the ingot from which the forging had been made had not been changed by the forging process or by subsequent heat treatment. And these are the people even now who consider themselves conservative, who would rather have their forgings made of a mild steel which is weak, than of a high-carbon steel which is strong, simply because the old ideas are not yet eradicated from their minds. Tests were made at the government testing bureau at Watertown by rapidly bending bars forward and backward within their elastic limit, with the following results, and these have given engineers an idea of the comparative endurance of wrought iron, steel and nickel steel, in such service as that to which crank pins, shafts, etc., are subject.

Tests of Steel Under Repeated Stresses.

Under a Fiber Stress of 40,000 Pounds per Square Inch.

Wrought iron breaks after   50,000 alternations of stress.

.15 p. c. carbon steel	"	"	170,000	"	"	"
.25 p. c.	"	"	"	"	229,000	"	"	"
.35 p. c.	"	"	"	"	317,000	"	"	"
.45 p. c.	"	"	"	"	976,000	"	"	"
3¼ p. c. nickel steel, carbon .25 to .30 p. c., 1,850,000 alternations of stress.
4½ p. c.	"	"	"	.25 to .30 p. c., 2,360,000	"	"	"
5½ p. c.	"	"	"	.25 to .30 p. c., 4,370,000	"	"	"

Charcoal.

The best qualities of charcoal are made from oak, maple, beech and chestnut. Between 5 and 17 per cent of coal will be obtained when the wood has been properly burned. A bushel of coal from hardwood weighs from 29 to 31 pounds and from pine 28 to 30 pounds.

Welding Powder for Iron and Steel.—For welding iron and steel a composition has lately been patented in Belgium, consisting of iron filings, 40 parts; borax, 20 parts; balsam of copaiba or some other resinous oil, 2 parts, and sal-ammoniac, 3 parts. They are mixed, heated and pulverized. The process of welding is much the same as usual. The surfaces to be welded are powdered with the composition and then brought to a cherry red heat, at which the powder melts, when the portions to be united are taken from the fire and joined. If the pieces to be welded are too large to be introduced at the same time into the forge, one can be first heated with the welding powder to a cherry red heat and then others afterward to a white heat, after which the welding may be effected.

To Make Edge-Tools from Cast-Steel and Iron.—This method consists in fixing a clean piece of wrought iron, brought to a welding heat, in the center of the mould, then pouring in melted steel, so as to entirely envelop the iron, and then forging the mass into the shape required.

To Weld Cast-Iron.

Take 3 parts of good class white sand, refined solution fostering and rock salt of each 1 part; heat the pieces to be welded in a charcoal fire, occasionally taking out and dipping into the composition, until they are of a proper heat to weld. Then take immediately to the anvil and weld together. If done carefully by one who understands welding iron, there will be a good strong weld.

Welding Composition for Cast-Steel.—Take borax, 10 parts; sal-ammoniac, 1 part; grind or pound them roughly together, then fuse them in a metal pot over a clear fire, taking care to continue the heat until the spume has disappeared from the surface. When the liquid appears clear, the composition is ready to be poured out to cool and concrete; afterward, being ground to a fine powder, it is ready for use. To use this composition, the steel to be welded is first raised to a bright yellow heat, it is then dipped into the welding powder, and again placed in the fire until it attains the same degree of heat as before; it is then ready to be placed under the hammer.

How to Restore Overheated Steel.

A number of receipts for compositions which will restore over-heated steel are given in the following:

To Restore Overheated Cast-Steel.—Take 1½ pounds borax, ½ pound sal-ammoniac, ¼ pound prussiate potash, 1 ounce rosin. Pound the above fine, add a gill each of water and alcohol. Put in an iron kettle, and boil until it becomes paste. Do not boil too long or it will become hard on cooling.

To Restore Overheated Steel.—Borax 3 pounds; sal-ammoniac, 1 pound; prussiate potash, ½ pound; alcohol, 1 gill; soft water, 1 pint. Put into an iron pan and hold over a slow fire until it comes to a slow boil and until the liquid matter evaporates; be careful to stir it well from the bottom and let it boil slow. This receipt is very valuable; no matter how badly the steel is over-heated it will restore and make it as durable as ever.

To Restore Overheated Steel and Improve Poor Steel.

Borax, 3 ounces; sal-ammoniac, 8 ounces; prussiate of potash, 3 ounces; blue clay, 2 ounces; rosin, 1½ pounds; water, 1 gill; alcohol, 1 gill. Put all over a slow fire; let it simmer until it dries to a powder. Heat the steel not above a cherry red; dip into this powder and afterwards hammer.

Composition to Toughen Steel.—Rosin 2½ pounds; tallow 2½ pounds; pitch 1½ pounds. Melt together and apply to the steel while hot.

Pointer.

Rosin on the blacksmith's forge improves and toughens steel. When the tool is hot, dip it into the rosin, then hammer.

To Weld Buggy Springs.

To weld buggy springs first scarf one piece of spring, and then weld onto it a piece of spring cut off about three-quarters of an inch longer than the first; heat and upset until one-quarter thicker at end than spring scarf. Now upset the other piece until as near thickness of first piece as possible; scarf and weld. Leave a trifle heavier at weld, and if the work has been done properly the weld can be warranted not to break. Use a 4½ pound hammer in making this weld, and keep at it until finished.

A French Welding Flux.

In using a flux, as is necessary when welding steel, or iron and steel, it is oftentimes difficult to keep the flux in place on

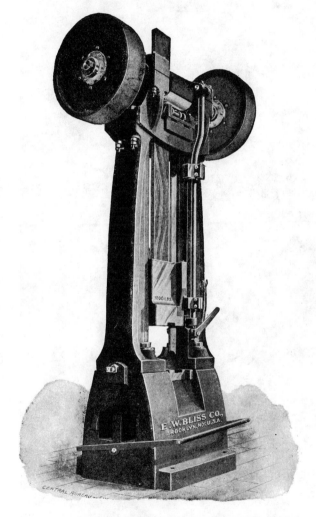

FIG. 128.—1,500-POUND FRICTION ROLL FORGING DROP WITH GEARLESS LIFTER.

account of its quickly melting and running off the weld. M. J. Lafitte, Paris, France, has devised a flux consisting of a borax mixture in which is incorporated a fine wire netting to hold it

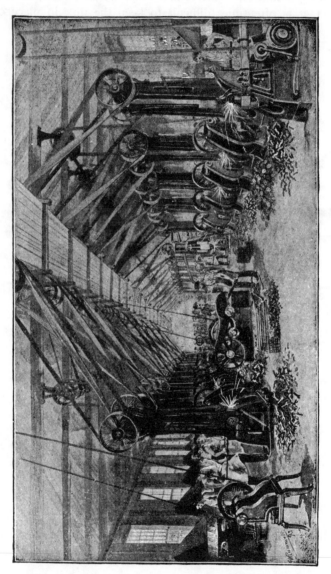

FIG. 129.—A DROP FORGING PLANT.

together. It is rolled out in thin sheets and divided into squares which are easily broken apart for use. Tests of steel specimens welded in the French government works show a remarkably high efficiency of the welds. This is due to the high protective power of the flux which prevents the formation of oxide on the surface of the welds.

Compound for Welding Steel.—The following composition has in a number of cases proved superior to borax for welding steel: Mix coarsely powdered borax with a thin paste of prussiate blue; then let it dry.

Fluxes for Soldering and Welding.

For iron or steel, borax or sal-ammoniac; tinned iron, rosin or chloride of zinc; copper and brass, sal-ammoniac or chloride zinc; zinc, chloride of zinc; lead, tallow or rosin; lead and tin pipes, rosin and sweet oil.

Substitute for Borax in Welding.

Copperas, 2 ounces; saltpeter, 1 ounce; common salt, 6 ounces; black oxide of manganese, 1 ounce; prussiate of potash, 1 ounce.

All pulverized and mixed with 3 pounds good welding sand.

High carbon steel can be welded with this at a lower heat than is required with borax.

Drop-Forgings.

Drop forging is the art of forging with drop hammers and may be designated as "machine blacksmithing." The inception of the art dates back to about 1853 when Colonel Samuel Coit adopted drop-hammers to make parts for firearms. The machines, processes and tools used in the art have since been greatly improved and the products of the drop forging industry are now used in a majority of the mechanical arts. Figs. 130 to 140 illustrate parts produced by drop forging.

The dies used for making drop-forgings are made in two parts. One part (the upper) is fastened in the ram or hammer of the drop, which moves vertically between two uprights or guides and is raised by means of friction rolls controlled by the operator. The other part of the die (the lower) is fixed in the anvil or base of the hammer. The ram raises until released, when it falls instantly, striking with the upper die the heated bar of metal placed on the bottom die and forcing it into impressions in both dies. By a series of such blows the complete article is formed.

An idea of the extensive use to which drop-forgings have been put may be gained from the fact that J. H. Williams & Co., of Brooklyn, N. Y., a company devoted exclusively to the making of drop-forgings, started in 1889 with a forging plant of three drop-hammers, and it now consists of forty-three drop-hammers, with trip-hammers, steam hammers, upsetting machines and other apparatus.

The necessary dies used to produce drop-forging of special shapes and sizes are usually made from a drawing or model, preferably the latter as it facilitates designing the dies and allows

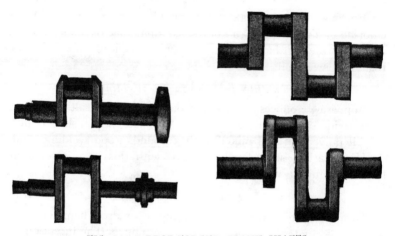

FIG. 130.—DROP-FORGED CRANK SHAFTS.

of figuring the cost of the tools much easier than could be done from a drawing.

In making drop-forging dies the die sinker must know whether the drawing and model show finished or forging size; he needs also to know the allowance desired in machining. It is usual to add 1-32 inch on each surface to be machined unless the piece is to be finished by grinding or polishing only, in which case 1-100 inch is allowed; surfaces not to be machined or ground are made close to size. Forgings vary slightly in thickness—say from 1-100 inch to 1-32 inch—depending on their shape and the material used. They can, however, be made to gage by a re-striking operation; this operation requires separate dies and entails additional expense.

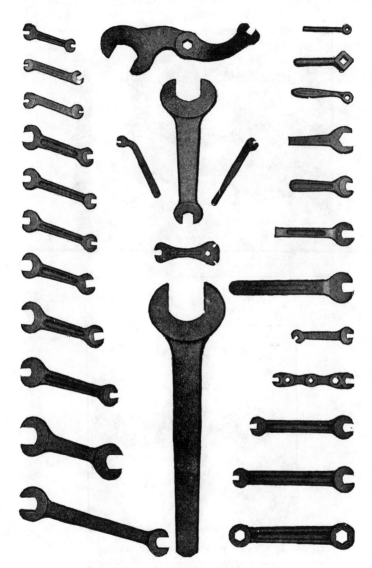

FIG. 131.—DROP-FORGED WRENCHES.

In addition to forging dies, the cost and endurance of which depend upon the work required of them, trimming dies are neces-

FIG. 132.—SPECIAL DROP-FORGINGS.

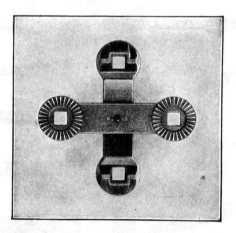

FIG. 133.—SPECIAL DROP-FORGING.

sary to remove the surplus metal thrown out between the forging dies in working.

Before using the finished set of dies for forging, a lead proof **is** struck up which is submitted to the customer. The proof often varies from the model or drawing by what is called draft. This is the taper necessary on the forgings to allow of drawing them from the dies while working, and it averages about seven degrees. It can be obtained by adding to or taking from the forging; usually the draft metal is added.

Establishments devoted exclusively to the manufacture of drop forgings carry a large and assorted stock of material from which to make the forgings. But in new dies, where the size of metal required cannot be determined until they are tried in the hammer, delays in obtaining the right sizes sometimes occur. As poor material cannot be used, drop-forgings are, therefore, not only superior to hand-forgings because the metal is improved by the

FIG. 134.—DROP-FORGED
GEAR.

FIG. 135.—DROP-FORGED
BRACKETS.

forging operation, but also because the nature of the process requires a good quality of material.

Forgings from steel of high carbon usually require annealing before they can be machined. While making drop-forgings they are carefully brushed with steel wire brushes to remove the scale, but if they are to be machined they are pickled in diluted sulphuric acid to insure the complete removal of the hard outer skin. Often small drop-forgings are tumbled instead of pickled.

Those who require drop-forgings will be saved undue expense if they inform manufacturers of the use for which the forgings are intended. The price is largely affected by the quantities made with one setting of the tools. It costs as much to set dies for 100 as for 1,000 pieces, and the forging work is also more costly in small lots. Prices for special drop-forging are made per piece, not per pound, and vary with the nature of the work, the material used and the quantity taken.

The cheapest drop-forgings in the long run are those most uniform in size and quality and close to finish dimensions, thus saving labor, time, tools and money.

Directions for Setting up Forging Drop-Hammers.

It is very important to have a good foundation, and we recommend as the cheapest and best, when it can be obtained, a log large enough in diameter at the butt end for the drop to stand on, and long enough to enter the ground six or eight feet.

FIG. 136.—SPECIAL DROP-FORGINGS.

FIG. 137.—DROP-FORGED BRACKET.

First dig a hole one foot deeper than is necessary to receive the log, and large enough to leave a space of about one foot all around it. Before the log is put into the hole, fill the bottom with grout one foot deep; then, after placing the log in the hole so that it will stand perpendicular, grout it nearly to the top of the ground.

For light drops, it will do very well to put a large flat stone under the bottom of the log and fill it with earth, well stamped down. Now adze the top of the log level; then make a depression in the center of the surface, about six inches square and two inches deep, with a groove about one inch wide leading to the edge of the block, to allow the scales and dirt to pass off, and not to get under the drop to make it rock or it will be unsteady. When, because of the size of the drop, or for other reasons, a log cannot be obtained large enough to put it on, take numbers, say one foot square, and bolt enough of them together to make it of suitable size, when set up on end to receive the drop. Grout, and fill in, in the same manner as for the log. Chestnut and oak are the best.

For forging drops with hammers weighing 1,000 to 2,000 pounds, some manufacturers build a masonry foundation 8 to 12 feet square at the base, tapering to the size of anvil shape at the top, and 10 to 14 feet deep, with about 4 feet in height of oak

FIG. 138.—DROP-FORGED
HOOK.

FIG. 139.—DROP-FORGED
YOKE.

FIG. 140.—DROP-FORGED
SHAFT BRACKET.

timbers at the top bolted together on end. The hole around this foundation is then filled with grouting. If only a rock or stone foundation can be had, place about one-half inch of sheet rubber or rubber belting under the bottom of the drop. There is danger of getting a foundation too solid for a drop. There should be some elasticity, and when set on a log or timber the desired effect is obtained; and when placed upon stone the rubber belting is sufficient. A suitable foundation having now been obtained, and the drop fastened to the same on a line with a shaft that is to drive it, brace the drop at the top by rods, one end of which can be secured to the building, and the other to the lifter, in holes provided for that purpose. The belts must run back away from the operator.

Government Use of Nickel Steel for Forgings.

With a view to their utilization in the various mechanical departments of the government of the United States, the Bureau of Steam Engineering has undertaken extensive experiments with various metals. One result already is the adoption of nickel steel for forgings and other parts of steam engines. It is contended that the principal advantage of nickel steel over ordinary carbon steel for forgings lies in the relation which the elastic limit bears to the tensile strength, the former being in a sense the true strength of the metal. The elastic limit of nickel steel is much higher than that of carbon steel of the same tensile strength and elongation, very often 30 per cent higher and in some cases as much as 50 per cent higher. The principal drawback to the commercial use of nickel steel has been the first cost of producing it, which in many cases is higher than the cost of ordinary finished forgings.

A decided virtue of nickel steel, according to government report, is the facility with which a low carbon steel will harden, it being the practice after a forging is forged and rough machined, to heat it and quench it in oil, which hardens it very much; afterward the forging is submitted to an annealing process which removes any strains set up in the metal by the sudden cooling which it receives. Nickel steel, after the first cost of production, is not much more expensive to forge than any carbon steel that runs over .40 per cent carbon, and about the same care is necessary in heating and forging as is required by a high carbon steel.

CHAPTER XI.

Increasing the Size of a Reamer When Worn.

To increase a reamer to size when worn, burnish the face of each tooth with a hardened burnisher, which can be made from a three-cornered file nicely polished on the corners. This will increase the size from 2 to 10 thousandths in diameter. Then hone back to the required size.

To make a tap or reamer cut larger than itself, put a piece of waste in one flute, enough to crowd it over and cut out on one side only. In larger sizes (1½ inch or over) put a strip of tin on one side and let it follow the tap through.

To Case-Harden Cast-Iron.

Heat to a red heat, roll in a composition consisting of equal parts of prussate of potash, sal-ammoniac and saltpeter, pulverized and thoroughly mixed. Plunge while yet hot into a bath containing 2 ounces of prussate of potash and 2 ounces of sal-ammoniac to each gallon of cold water.

Rules for Calculating Speed.

The diameter of driven given to find its number of revolutions:

Rule.—Multiply the diameter of the driver by its number of revolutions and divide the product by the diameter of the driven. The quotient will be the number of revolutions of the driven.

The diameter and revolutions of the driver being given to find the diameter of the driven that shall make any number of revolutions:

Rule.—Multiply the diameter of the driver by its number of revolutions and divide the product by the number of required revolutions of the driven. The quotient will be its diameter.

To ascertain the size of pulleys for given speeds:

Rule.—Multiply all the diameters of the drivers together and all the diameters of driven together; divide the drivers by the driven. Multiply the answer by the known number of revolutions of main shaft.

Improved Soldering or Tinning Acid.

Muriatic acid 1 pound; put into it all the zinc it will dissolve and 1 ounce of sal-ammoniac, then it is ready for use.

Lubricant for Water Cuts.

Strong sal soda water or soap water is much better than clear water to use where water cuts are being taken, either on lathe or planer.

Babbitting.

Put a piece of rosin the size of a walnut into your Babbitt; stir thoroughly, then skim. It makes poor Babbitt run better, and improves it. Babbitt heated just hot enough to light a pine stick will run in places with the rosin in, where, without it, it would not. It is also claimed that rosin will prevent blowing when pouring in damp boxes.

Laying Out Work.

In laying out work on planed or smooth surfaces of steel or iron, use blue vitriol and water on the surface. This will copper-over the surface nicely, so that all lines will show plainly. If on oily surfaces, add a little oil of vitriol; this will eat the oil off and leave a nicely coppered surface.

Lubricant for Working Aluminum.

Use kerosene oil (coal oil) for drilling or turning aluminum.

To Prevent Rust.

To prevent rust on tools, use vaseline, to which a small amount of powdered gum camphor has been added; heat together over a slow fire.

Lubricant for Drilling Hard Steel.

Use turpentine instead of oil when drilling hard steel, saw plates, etc. It will drill readily when you could not touch it with oil.

Coppering Polished Steel Surfaces.

To copper the surface of iron or steel wire, have the wire perfectly clean, then wash with the following solution, when it will present at once a coppered surface: Rain water, 3 pounds; sulphate of copper, 1 pound.

To Blue Steel Without Heating.

To blue steel without heating, apply nitric acid; then wipe off the acid, clean, oil and burnish.

To Remove Scale from Steel.

Scale may be removed from steel articles by pickling in water with a little sulphuric acid in it, and when the scale is loosened, brushing it with sand and stiff brush.

To Distinguish Wrought and Cast-Iron from Steel.

Elsiner produces a bright surface by polishing or filing, and applies a drop of nitric acid, which is allowed to remain there for one or two minutes, and then washed off with water. The spot will look a pale ashy gray on wrought-iron, a brownish black on steel, a deep black on cast-iron. It is the carbon present in various proportions which produces the difference in appearance.

Anti-Friction Alloy for Journal Boxes.

Zinc, 17 parts; copper, 1 part; antimony, ½ part.

This possesses unsurpassable anti-friction qualities and does not require the protection of outer castings of the harder metal.

Solder for Aluminum.

A great drawback to the use of aluminum for many purposes is the difficulty of soldering it. A number of solders are known that are fairly successful when manipulated by skillful hands. The following one was recommended by Prof. E. Wilson in a paper read before the Society of Arts. The constituents are 28 pounds block-tin, 3.5 pounds lead, 7 pounds spelter, and 14 pounds phosphor-tin. The phosphor-tin should contain 10 per cent phosphor. The following instructions should be followed when soldering aluminum: Clean off all dirt and grease from the surface of the metal with benzine, apply the solder with a copper bit, and when the molten solder covers the surface of the metal, scratch through the solder with a wire brush, by which means the oxide is broken and taken up. Quick manipulation is necessary.

Case-Hardening with Kerosene.

There is a process of hardening steel by petroleum which is

not generally known. The article to be treated is first thoroughly rubbed with ordinary washing soap, and then placed in a charcoal fire and heated to a cherry red. Then it is plunged into petroleum. There is no fear of the oil igniting, but it is wise not to have a naked light too near. Parts hardened by this method are said to have no cracks nor do they warp, and after hardening, owing to being white, can be finished without any cleaning or grinding.

Case-Hardening Cones and Cups.

For case-hardening small pieces, such as the cups and cones used in bicycle bearings, the following method has been found to work well in practice. It is somewhat different from the usual plan followed by case-hardeners in bicycle factories: First, surround the article with yellow prussate of potash, then with leather (old boots will do), then with clay, and pack in an iron box of some sort, usually a piece of gas pipe. Plug up the ends with clay; place the whole in the fire and keep at a red heat for four or five hours, then quench in water. The usual difficulty with workers in a small way is to keep the articles at a uniform temperature for such a long time.

Drills.

As a rule, the cutting edges of twist drills are formed with a cutter of correct form to produce a radial line of cutting edge; thus a different form of cutter is required for milling the flutes of straight flute drills.

Drills are generally made of .002-inch or .003-inch taper per foot for clearance and have the major part of land on the periphery ground away for the same purpose, about .003 inch on a side.

Drills for brass should be made with straight flutes; those for cast-iron and tool-steel should in most cases have spiral flutes, at an angle of about 16 deg.; soft steel, 22 deg.

Chucking drills, for use on cored holes, or as followers of solid twist drills, are quite often provided with from three to eight flutes; the latter, on large work, are very efficient. Care should be taken in grinding, to insure all teeth cutting simultaneously. These tools are made of solid, shell, and inserted type.

The inserted type are preferable for straight flutes over 2¾ inches, and for angular flutes over 4 inches, on account of cost.

For drilling a large hole in a spindle the latter should be supported in a back rest, and the drill entered through a drill bushing to start perfectly true. Then, by using a drill with one cutting edge and ground on the outside, a long, straight hole may be readily produced. An ordinary twist drill will do practically the same if the center is made female, the only objection being that this form is much more difficult to grind.

Reamer Practice.

The following particulars in regard to the experience of the well known American firm, the Lodge & Shipley Machine Company, in making and using reamers, were given by their Mr. William Lodge:

The only reamer we use that is out of the ordinary is a taper reamer made with only three blades. These are cut as deep as the strength of the stock will permit and have very little clearance, which is obtained by grinding the blades convex—not flat or hollow—as shown in Fig. 141. The reamer is used where a consider-

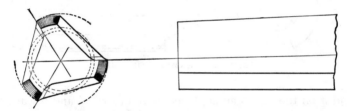

FIG. 141.—TAPER REAMER WITH THREE BLADES.

able amount of metal is to be removed. For instance, we would bore a hole of the right size for the small end of the reamer and then move it up so that it would cut a length anywhere from three to six inches, feeding very rapidly. We have bored thousands of holes with this style of reamer, getting the best results we ever obtained with the least trouble and in the quickest time.

Many reamers are in use that are known as "home-made," that is, made by the parties themselves. We have found a great mistake in such reamers. It often occurs that the flutes are cut too shallow and the spacing is entirely too close; that they are evenly spaced instead of staggered, and very often have an even number of teeth, all of which is likely to cause chattering and breaking of taper reamers. An evenly spaced reamer will begin to chatter the moment the cutting edge refuses to cut, especially when cutting steel and when evenly spaced, one blade will jump into the space or chatter mark made by the blade in advance of it. Another serious fault with any reamer, either straight or taper, is too much clearance. This will invariably cause a reamer to chatter.

As to reamers for brass, we never make them oversize, and we always make the blade of the reamer for brass the same as we would grind a tool for cutting brass, namely, instead of using a radial line on the center as in other cutting tools, we throw the cutting edge of the blade off from the center at an angle of at least 20 degrees out of the radial line, as shown in Fig. 142. Thus, in turning brass, if you had a tool that was ground straight and mounted it in the tool post exactly at the center of the work you would find that the tool would chatter. Take the same tool and

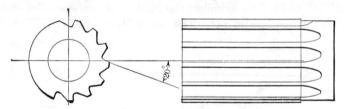

FIG. 142.—REAMER FOR BRASS.

grind it on the top to an angle as above described and toward the underside of the blade, and it would cut quite freely and without any chattering. At all times, however, it is necessary to keep the cutting edge of the reamer for brass extremely sharp, because the very moment the cutting edge is dull it will begin to bind and scream sufficiently loud to drive you out of the shop. Reamers for reaming brass require twice or three times the attention in keeping to a sharp edge that other reamers require.

For hand reaming we never have to exceed 3-1000 in any material, and all our machine reaming is done by a reamer with very much coarser blades than the ordinary commercial reamer. They are made so that they may be ground on the points, are fed rapidly, and the tool used in advance of them leaves in no case less than 1-32 and often as much as 1-16.

Reamers and Reaming.

In order to ream uniform holes (as regards diameter) in a

screw machine, it is necessary to always have an equal amount of stock for the reamer to remove. This can be best accomplished by using two reamers, one for roughing, and one for finishing. The roughing reamer should be preceded by a single pointed boring tool (or its equivalent), to insure a true hole. On thin work a finishing reamer should be of "rose form," so as to be self-supporting and prevent enlargement of the hole by its weight.

For steel, reamers are ground straight, while for cast-iron, brass and copper it often becomes necessary to grind same slightly back tapering to prevent roughing up.

The teeth on reamers for steel and cast-iron should be on center, while for brass they should be slightly ahead of the center.

On machine reaming, when possible to do so, the reamers are hung loose and allowed to follow the true or concentric hole made by a single-pointed boring tool. This can be done by having a "floating" reamer with a pin entered through the holder and the reamer at the back end, the hole in the reamer being larger than the pin so as to allow it to find its own center.

Square reamers (scrapers) are often used for fine finishing, especially on brass. Expansion reamers possess many desirable features; but there are few, if any, that can be adjusted and used for sizing, without grinding the cutting edges each time they are expanded, as unless perfectly fitted in as regards tapers, etc., the separate teeth do not expand equally.

As a matter of cost, however, this additional grinding amounts to but little in comparison with that of a new solid or shell reamer of large diameter, two and a fourth inches or more.

Number of Teeth Generally Milled in Reamers.

3-16 to $\frac{5}{8}$ inch diameter, 6 teeth.

$\frac{5}{8}$ to $1\frac{1}{4}$ inches diameter, 8 teeth.

$1\frac{1}{4}$ to $1\frac{1}{2}$ inches diameter, 10 teeth.

$1\frac{1}{2}$ to $2\frac{3}{8}$ inches diameter, 12 teeth.

$2\frac{3}{8}$ to 3 inches diameter, 14 teeth.

3 to 4 inches diameter, 16 teeth.

4 to 5 inches diameter, 18 teeth.

A long hole can be reamed straight by pulling back slightly after the reamer has commenced to cut.

On Babbitt, reamers of the usual form are used, with the exception that the point is ground tapering about $\frac{1}{2}$-inch long, to a diameter equal to size generated by boring tool. This gives a smooth hole, free from lines, also prevents rings. Left-hand spiral flutes are recommended.

On taper reamers for screw machine, use 2¼ inches per foot and upward. They will cut much easier if made with left-hand spiral flutes or angle, but on account of difficulty in grinding this is not often done.

For forming or curving reamers for projectile work, the above holds good. Reamers 1½ to 2¼ inches taper per foot should have flute straight for finishers, the roughers either of the deep form or with a left-hand spiral thread nicked around. The reamers to 1½ inches taper per foot are fluted left-hand to prevent drawing in when cutting.

Roughing, taper and forming reamers are sometimes made from steel with an undercut, and also with right-hand spiral, and they remove the stock very rapidly.

Speeds for reaming should range from 20 to 30 per cent less than turning and drilling speeds. (See tables, pages 123 and 124.)

On large taper reamers, with slight taper, it has been found good practice to make each tooth a different left-hand spiral and also to "stagger" the teeth as regards spacing.

Rose reamers are quite often ground tapering, that is, small at back, .003 to foot, and then are less liable to rough up the hole they are reaming, and give a straight hole very nearly correct in diameter.

Grinding Twist Drills.

Grinding twist drills accurately is generally admitted to be difficult. To know the number of revolutions a drill should run is of great importance in order to obtain the most economical results. The illustration, Fig. 143, shows opposite sides of the Standard Twist Drill Grinding Gage, made of steel 1-16-inch thick. The angle of the gage is ground to exactly 59 degrees. The scale on the gage is graduated so that the cutting edges of the drill can be measured and ground exactly the same length. The straight edge of the gage is a 2-inch scale graduated by eighths of an inch; opposite each eighth mark is a number, which is the best speed to run a drill of corresponding size of diameter.

In using the gage, hold it with the left hand and place the drill in the gage with the cutting edges of the drill facing you. The rest of the lip of the drill must be lower than the cutting edge, which will give the drill clearance and allow the edges to cut. Always keep *Twist Drills sharp* and run them at the *proper speed.* If you want to force a drill to do work quickly, run at the right speed, but *increase the feed.*

Circular Forming Tools.

Circular forming tools for machine steel and cast-iron should have a generous amount of clearance.

Care must be taken on particular forms, when forming cutters are not on center, that they are formed with this point taken into consideration.

Forming cutters with steps having great difference of diam-

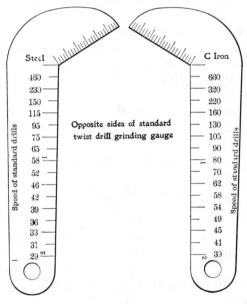

Steel		C Iron
460		660
230		320
150		220
115		160
95	Opposite sides of standard	130
75	twist drill grinding gauge	105
65		90
58		80
52		70
46		62
42		58
39		54
36		49
33		45
31		41
29		39

Speed of standard drills (left) · *Speed of standard drills* (right)

FIG. 143.

eter, and also with sharp corners, if made in sections, harden more easily and safely.

Circular threading tools for inside threading must be much smaller than the work; about one-third is the proper practice.

Care should be exercised to use a correct angle of chaser.

Plain Forming Tools.

Plain forming tools should have a clearance of from 6½ to 10 degrees.

Rake: Machinery steel 8 to 13 degrees.

Rake: Tool steel, medium, 6 to 9 degrees.

Rake: Brass, none.

The clearance on tools for brass is quite often stoned off its cutting edge to prevent "biting in" (due to ease of cutting) and then chattering, due to great thickness of chip and consequent difficulty in severing. The "stoning off" also tends to act as a support for the cutter.

Facing.

For steel and cast-iron, cutters with from 6 to 12 degrees rake cut very freely. The clearance should be from 3½ to 10 degrees; when there is any tendency to chatter, the cutting edge should be stoned on clearance face sufficiently to prevent "biting in." On very broad work it often becomes necessary to make cutters without any rake or angle, but allow scraping, to prevent chatter.

In practice it is found advantageous to place cutter ahead of center, exposing a larger cutting edge to work, giving thinner chip.

In multiple or inserted cutter heads, it is well to unevenly space the cutters; as a precaution against chattering, have the cutters "staggered."

Use machines with large bearings, and with chucks close to same, for good results.

Lubricant in Milling Steel or Wrought Iron.

In milling steel or wrought iron, keep cutter thoroughly wet with lubricant. Sal soda dissolved in water is often used. A better lubricant for milling cutter, drill, etc., is: Lard oil, ½ gallon; whale oil soap, 2 pounds; sal soda, 3 pounds; water, 10 gallons. Have the soap so it will dissolve readily. Boil the whole until dissolved.

Counterboring.

For cast-iron and steel, counterbores are generally made with ten to sixteen degrees angle, i. e., spiral; for brass they are cut straight. Clearance is from five to ten degrees. On brass, "stone" the clearance edge to prevent chattering.

Counterbores internally lubricated are recommended for steel for use to depth of one-half of the diameter or more.

Angle clearance on all tools must be more than spiral generated by feed, at smallest diameter of cutting point plus sufficient to be really forced in work (about 3 degrees).

Soldering.

There are many kinds of solders, from that which will melt in boiling water to hard brass solder that melts only at white heat. As a rule, the harder the solder the stronger the joint. Of the white solders silver is the hardest. For all solders that require a red heat, borax is used as a flux, and the solder will run anywhere the borax goes. Rubbing the joint with a pointed piece of iron will help the solder to run into the joint. The parts to be soldered should, of course, be cleaned. The solder will not stick to the work until the surface of the work is heated to the melting point of the solder. Don't try to solder with a cold iron, and, with

FIG. 144.—COUNTERBORE.

FIG. 145.—COUNTERSINK.

large pieces, heat them to the melting point of the solder or use a very hot iron. Always use a solder with a much lower melting point than that of the metal to be soldered.

Useful Information.

Doubling the diameter of a pipe increases its capacity four times.

A cubic foot of water weighs 62½ pounds, and contains 1,728 cubic inches, or 7½ gallons.

A gallon of fresh water weighs 8 1-3 pounds, and contains 231 cubic inches.

To find the capacity of a cylinder in gallons: Multiply the area in inches by the height of stroke in inches. Divide this product by 231 (being the cubical contents of a gallon in inches); the quotient is the capacity in gallons.

To find the area of a circle or cylinder: Square the diameter in inches and multiply the product by .7854.

Example: What is the area of a 12-inch circle?

$12 \times 12 = 144 + .7854 = 113.0976$ square inches.

Rust joint cement (quick setting): 1 part sal-ammoniac in powder (by weight), 2 flour of sulphur, 80 iron borings, made to a paste with water.

Rust joint (slow setting): 2 parts sal-ammoniac, 1 flour of sulphur, 200 iron borings.

The latter is best if joint is not required for immediate use.

Metal to expand in cooling: 9 parts lead, 2 antimony, 1 bismuth.

Glue to resist moisture: 1 pound of glue in 2 quarts of skimmed milk.

To color or coat zinc: Dissolve 1 ounce blue vitriol in 4 ounces water, add teaspoonful nitric acid. Apply with cloth.

Lacquer for Brass Articles.

A good lacquer for brass articles is made from best orange shellac dissolved in a good alcohol (1 to 2 ounces gum to the pint) and filtered through filter paper. This is excellent for brass, and for silver the bleached shellac may be substituted. Some prefer to use the lacquer thin and the work heated to about 115 degrees Fahr., a temperature that will vaporize the alcohol and leave a firmly adhering coat of gum if the work has been properly cleansed.

Removing Rust from Polished Steel and Iron.

In the Journal of the United States Artillery directions were given for caring for ordnance, and the treatment recommended for rust on polished steel is as follows: Cyanide of potash is most excellent for removing rust, and should be made much use of. Instruments of polished steel may be cleaned as follows: First soak, if possible, in a solution of cyanide of potassium in the proportion of one ounce of cyanide to four ounces of water. Allow this to act till all loose rust and scale is removed and then polish with cyanide soap.

The cyanide soap referred to is made as follows: Potassium cyanide, precipitated chalk, white Castile soap. Make a saturated solution of the cyanide and add chalk sufficient to make a creamy paste. Add the soap cut in fine shavings and thoroughly incorporate in a mortar. When the mixture is stiff cease to add soap. It may be well to state that potassium cyanide is a violent poison.

For removing rust from iron the following is given: Iron may be quickly and easily cleaned by dipping in or washing with nitric acid, one part; muriatic acid, one part; water, twelve parts. After using wash with clean water.

Miscellaneous Information.

Area of a circle = diameter × .7854.

Circumference of a circle = diameter × 3.1416.

Given the area of a circle to find the diameter, divide the area by .7854 and extract the square root.

Area of a hexagon = length of one side × 2.598.

Cubic contents in inches of a bar of iron = area of one end in inches by its length, in inches.

Weight of cast iron, per cubic inch, .26 pound; of wrought iron, .278; of steel, .283; of copper and bronze, .32; of brass, .3.

A wrought-iron bar one square inch in section and one yard long weighs 10 pounds. Steel is about two per cent heavier than wrought iron. Cast iron is about six per cent lighter than wrought iron.

To find the surface speed in feet per minute of an emery wheel or milling cutter: Divide the number of revolutions of the wheel per minute by 12, and multiply the result by 3.1416 times the diameter of the emery wheel in inches.

To find the number of revolutions a wheel must run for a given surface speed, multiply the surface speed in feet per minute by 12 and divide the result by 3.1416 times the diameter in inches.

Given, the diameter of a hexagon nut across the flats, to find the diameter across corners, multiply the diameter across flats by 1.156.

TABLE OF DECIMAL EQUIVALENTS OF MILLIMETERS AND
FRACTIONS OF MILLIMETERS.

$\frac{1}{100}$ mm. = .0003937 inch.

MM	Inches	MM	Inches	MM	Inches
$\frac{1}{50}$	.00079	$\frac{26}{50}$	.02047	2	.07874
$\frac{2}{50}$	.00157	$\frac{27}{50}$	.02126	3	.11811
$\frac{3}{50}$	.00236	$\frac{28}{50}$	.02205	4	.15748
$\frac{4}{50}$	.00315	$\frac{29}{50}$	.02283	5	.19685
$\frac{5}{50}$	.00394	$\frac{30}{50}$	.02362	6	.23622
$\frac{6}{50}$	.00472	$\frac{31}{50}$	.02441	7	.27559
$\frac{7}{50}$	.00551	$\frac{32}{50}$	.02520	8	.31496
$\frac{8}{50}$	.00630	$\frac{33}{50}$	.02598	'9	.35433
$\frac{9}{50}$	.00709	$\frac{34}{50}$	.02677	10	.39370
$\frac{10}{50}$	.00787	$\frac{35}{50}$	.02756	11	.43307
$\frac{11}{50}$	.00866	$\frac{36}{50}$	.02835	12	.47244
$\frac{12}{50}$	.00945	$\frac{37}{50}$	.02913	13	.51181
$\frac{13}{50}$	.01024	$\frac{38}{50}$	.02992	14	.55118
$\frac{14}{50}$	.01102	$\frac{39}{50}$	.03071	15	.59055
$\frac{15}{50}$	.01181	$\frac{40}{50}$	.03150	16	.62992
$\frac{16}{50}$	.01260	$\frac{41}{50}$	.03228	17	.66929
$\frac{17}{50}$	.01339	$\frac{42}{50}$	.03307	18	.70866
$\frac{18}{50}$	.01417	$\frac{43}{50}$	.03386	19	.74803
$\frac{19}{50}$	.01496	$\frac{44}{50}$	.03465	20	.78740
$\frac{20}{50}$	.01575	$\frac{45}{50}$	.03543	21	.82677
$\frac{21}{50}$	.01654	$\frac{46}{50}$	.03622	22	.86614
$\frac{22}{50}$	.01732	$\frac{47}{50}$	.03701	23	.90551
$\frac{23}{50}$	.01811	$\frac{48}{50}$	.03780	24	.94488
$\frac{24}{50}$	.01890	$\frac{49}{50}$	.03858	25	.98425
$\frac{25}{50}$	.01969	I	.03937	26	1.02362

10   mm. = 1 centimeter = 0.3937 inches.
10   cm. = 1 decimeter = 3.937   inches.
10   dm. = 1 meter   = 39.37   inches.
25.4 mm. = 1 English inch.

DECIMAL EQUIVALENTS OF PARTS OF AN INCH.

$\frac{1}{64}$	.01563	$\frac{21}{64}$	.32813	$\frac{45}{64}$	.70313
$\frac{1}{32}$	.03125	$\frac{11}{32}$	.34375	$\frac{23}{32}$	.71875
$\frac{3}{64}$	.04688	$\frac{23}{64}$	.35938	$\frac{47}{64}$	.73438
$\frac{1}{16}$	.0625	$\frac{3}{8}$	.375	$\frac{3}{4}$	.75
$\frac{5}{64}$	.07813	$\frac{25}{64}$	.39063	$\frac{49}{64}$	.76563
$\frac{3}{32}$	.09375	$\frac{13}{32}$	.40625	$\frac{25}{32}$	.78125
$\frac{7}{64}$	.10938	$\frac{27}{64}$	.42188	$\frac{51}{64}$	.79688
$\frac{1}{8}$	.125	$\frac{7}{16}$	.4375	$\frac{13}{16}$	.8125
$\frac{9}{64}$	.14063	$\frac{29}{64}$	.45313	$\frac{53}{64}$	.82813
$\frac{5}{32}$	.15625	$\frac{15}{32}$	.46875	$\frac{27}{32}$	.84375
$\frac{11}{64}$	.17188	$\frac{31}{64}$	.48438	$\frac{55}{64}$	.85938
$\frac{3}{16}$	.1875	$\frac{1}{2}$	.5	$\frac{7}{8}$	.875
$\frac{13}{64}$	.20313	$\frac{33}{64}$	.51563	$\frac{57}{64}$	.89063
$\frac{7}{32}$	.21875	$\frac{17}{32}$	.53125	$\frac{29}{32}$	.90625
$\frac{15}{64}$	.23438	$\frac{35}{64}$	.54688	$\frac{59}{64}$	.92188
$\frac{1}{4}$	.25	$\frac{9}{16}$	.5625	$\frac{15}{16}$	.9375
$\frac{17}{64}$	.26063	$\frac{37}{64}$	.57813	$\frac{61}{64}$	.95313
$\frac{9}{32}$	.28125	$\frac{19}{32}$	.59375	$\frac{31}{32}$	.96875
$\frac{19}{64}$	.29688	$\frac{39}{64}$	.60938	$\frac{63}{64}$	.98438
$\frac{5}{16}$	.3125	$\frac{5}{8}$	.625	1	1.00000
		$\frac{41}{64}$	.64063		
		$\frac{21}{32}$	.65625		
		$\frac{43}{64}$	.67188		
		$\frac{11}{16}$	.6875		

CONSTANTS FOR FINDING DIAMETER AT BOTTOM OF THREAD.

Threads per Inch.	U. S. Standard Constant.	V Thread Constant.	Threads per Inch.	U. S. Standard Constant.	V Thread Constant.
64	.02029	.02706	16	.08118	.10825
60	.02165	.02887	14	.09278	.12357
56	.02319	.03093	13	.09992	.13323
50	.02598	.03464	12	.10825	.14433
48	.02706	.03608	11	.11809	.15745
44	.02952	.03936	10	.12990	.17320
40	.03247	.04330	9	.14433	.19244
36	.03608	.04811	8	.16237	.21650
32	.04059	05412	7	.18555	.24742
30	.04330	.05773	6	.21650	.28866
28	.04639	.06185	5½	.23618	.31490
26	.04996	06661	5	.25980	.34650
24	.05412	07216	4½	.28866	.38488
22	.05904	.07872	4	.32475	.43300
20	06495	.08660	3½	.37114	.49485
18	07216	09622	3	43333	.57733

$C =$ Constant for number of threads per inch.

$D =$ Outside diameter.

$D^1 =$ Diameter at bottom of thread.

$$D^1 = D - C.$$

EXAMPLE.—Given outside diameter of U. S. S. screw thread, 2 inches, 4½ threads per inch; find diameter at bottom of thread. $D = 2$ inches; for 4½ threads U. S. S. constant, $C = .2886$; then diameter at bottom of thread $D^1 = 2 - .2886 = 1.7114$ inches.

METRIC AND ENGLISH OR AMERICAN (U. S.) EQUIVALENT MEASURES.

Measures of Length.

1 meter $= \begin{cases} 39.37 \text{ inches.} \\ 3.28083 \text{ feet.} \\ 1.0936 \text{ yds.} \end{cases}$

1 centimeter $= .3937$ inch.

1 millimeter $= \begin{cases} .03937 \text{ inch, or} \\ \frac{1}{25} \text{ inch nearly.} \end{cases}$

1 kilometer $= 0.62137$ mile.

1 foot $= .3048$ meter.

1 inch $= \begin{cases} 2.54 \text{ centimeters.} \\ 25.4 \text{ millimeters.} \end{cases}$

Measures of Surface.

1 square meter $= \begin{cases} 10.764 \text{ square feet.} \\ 1.196 \text{ square yds.} \end{cases}$

1 square centimeter $= 155$ sq. in.
1 square millimeter $= .00155$ sq. in.

1 square yard $= .836$ square meter.
1 square foot $= .0929$ square meter.

1 square in. $= \begin{cases} 6.452 \text{ sq. centimeters.} \\ 645.2 \text{ sq. millimeters.} \end{cases}$

Measures of Volume and Capacity

1 cubic meter $= \begin{cases} 35 \ 314 \text{ cubic feet.} \\ 1.308 \text{ cubic yards.} \\ 264.2 \text{ gallons (231 cubic inch).} \end{cases}$

1 cubic decimeter $= \begin{cases} 61.023 \text{ cubic in.} \\ .0353 \text{ cubic ft.} \end{cases}$

1 cubic centimeter $= .061$ cubic inch.

1 liter $= \begin{cases} 1 \text{ cubic decimeter.} \\ 61.023 \text{ cubic inches.} \\ .0353 \text{ cubic foot.} \\ 1.0567 \text{ quarts (U. S.)} \\ .2642 \text{ gallons (U. S.)} \\ 2.202 \text{ lbs. of water at } 62°F. \end{cases}$

1 cubic yard $= .7645$ cubic meter.

1 cubic ft. $= \begin{cases} .02832 \text{ cubic meter.} \\ 28.317 \text{ cubic decimeters} \\ 28.317 \text{ liters.} \end{cases}$

1 cubic inch $= 16 \ 387$ cubic centimeters.
1 gallon (British) $= 4 \ 543$ liters.
1 gallon (U. S.) $= 3.785$ liters.

Measures of Weight.

1 gram $= 15.432$ grains.
1 kilogram $= 2.2046$ pounds.

1 metric ton $= \begin{cases} .9842 \text{ ton of } 2240 \text{ lbs.} \\ 19.68 \text{ cwts.} \\ 2204.6 \text{ lbs.} \end{cases}$

1 grain $= .0648$ gram.
1 ounce avoirdupois $= 28.35$ grams.
1 pound $= .4536$ kilograms.

1 ton of 2240 lbs. $= \begin{cases} 1.016 \text{ metric tons.} \\ 1016 \text{ kilograms.} \end{cases}$

Miscellaneous.

1 kilogram per meter $= .6720$ pounds per foot.
1 gram per square millimeter $= 1.422$ pounds per square inch.
1 kilogram per square meter $= 0.2084$ " " foot.
1 kilogram per cubic meter $= .0624$ " cubic "
1 degree centigrade $= 1.8$ degrees Fahrenheit.
1 pound per foot $= 1.488$ kilograms per meter.
1 pound per square foot $= 4.882$ kilograms per square meter.
1 pound per cubic foot $= 16.02$ kilograms per cubic meter.
1 degree Fahrenheit $= .5556$ degrees centigrade.
1 Calorie (French Thermal Unit) $= 3.968$ B. T. U. (British Thermal Unit).

1 Horse Power $= \begin{cases} 33,000 \text{ foot pounds per minute.} \\ 746 \text{ Watts.} \end{cases}$

1 Watt (Unit of Electrical Power) $= \begin{cases} .00134 \text{ Horse Power.} \\ 44.24 \text{ foot pounds per minute.} \end{cases}$

1 Kilowatt $= \begin{cases} 1000 \text{ Watts.} \\ 1.34 \text{ Horse Power} \\ 44240 \text{ foot pounds per minute.} \end{cases}$

WEIGHTS AND AREAS OF ROUND, SQUARE AND HEXAGON
STEEL.

Weight of one cubic inch = .2836 lbs.

Weight of one cubic foot = 490 lbs.

Thickness or Diameter.	Area = Diam.² x .7854. Round.			Area = Side² x 1. Square.		Area = Diam.²x.866 Hexagon.	
	Weight Per Inch.	Area Square Inches.	Circum-ference Inches.	Weight Per Inch.	Area Square Inches.	Weight Per Inch.	Area Square Inches.
1/32	.0002	.0008	.0981	.0003	.0010	.0002	.0008
1/16	.0009	.0031	.1963	.0011	.0039	.0010	.0034
3/32	.0020	.0069	.2995	.0025	.0088	.0022	.0076
1/8	.0035	.0123	.3927	.0044	.0156	.0038	.0135
5/32	.0054	.0192	.4908	.0069	.0244	.0060	.0211
3/16	.0078	.0276	.5890	.0101	.0352	.0086	.0304
7/32	.0107	.0376	.6872	.0136	.0479	.0118	.0414
1/4	.0139	.0491	.7854	.0177	.0625	.0154	.0540
9/32	.0176	.0621	.8835	.0224	.0791	.0194	.0686
5/16	.0218	.0767	.9817	.0277	.0977	.0240	.0846
11/32	.0263	.0928	1.0799	.0335	.1182	.0290	.1023
3/8	.0313	.1104	1.1781	.0405	.1406	.0345	.1218
13/32	.0368	.1296	1.2762	.0466	.1651	.0405	.1428
7/16	.0426	.1503	1.3744	.0543	.1914	.0470	.1658
15/32	.0489	.1726	1.4726	.0623	.2197	.0540	.1903
1/2	.0557	.1963	1.5708	.0709	.2500	.0614	.2161
17/32	.0629	.2217	1.6689	.0800	.2822	.0693	.2444
9/16	.0705	.2485	1.7671	.0897	.3164	.0777	.2743
19/32	.0785	.2769	1.8653	.1036	.3526	.0866	.3053
5/8	.0870	.3068	1.9635	.1108	.3906	.0959	.3383
21/32	.0959	.3382	2.0616	.1221	.4307	.1058	.3730
11/16	.1053	.3712	2.1598	.1340	.4727	.1161	.4093
23/32	.1151	.4057	2.2580	.1465	.5166	.1270	.4474
3/4	.1253	.4418	2.3562	.1622	.5625	.1382	.4871
25/32	.1359	.4794	2.4543	.1732	.6103	.1499	.5286
13/16	.1470	.5185	2.5525	.1872	.6602	.1620	.5712
27/32	.1586	.5591	2.6507	.2019	.7119	.1749	.6165
7/8	.1705	.6013	2.7489	.2171	.7656	.1880	.6631
29/32	.1829	.6450	2.8470	.2329	.8213	.2015	.7112
15/16	.1958	.6903	2.9452	.2492	.8789	.2159	.7612
31/32	.2090	.7371	3.0434	.2661	.9384	.2305	.8127
1	.2227	.7854	3.1416	.2836	1.0000	.2456	.8643
1 1/16	.2515	.8866	3.3379	.3201	1.1289	.2773	.9776
1 1/8	.2819	.9940	3.5343	.3589	1.2656	.3109	1.0973
1 3/16	.3141	1.1075	3.7306	.4142	1.4102	.3464	1.2212
1 1/4	.3480	1.2272	3.9270	.4431	1.5625	.3838	1.3531
1 5/16	.3837	1.3530	4.1233	.4885	1.7227	.4231	1.4919
1 3/8	.4211	1.4849	4.3197	.5362	1.8906	.4643	1.6373
1 7/16	.4603	1.6230	4.5160	.5860	2.0664	.5076	1.7898
1 1/2	.5012	1.7671	4.7124	.6487	2.2500	.5526	1.9485
1 9/16	.5438	1.9175	4.9087	.6930	2.4414	.5996	2.1143
1 5/8	.5882	2.0739	5.1051	.7489	2.6406	.6480	2.2847
1 11/16	.6343	2.2365	5.3014	.8076	2.8477	.6994	2.4662
1 3/4	.6821	2.4058	5.4978	.8685	3.0625	.7521	2.6522

WEIGHTS AND AREAS OF ROUND, SQUARE AND HEXAGON STEEL.

Continued.

Thickness or Diam.	Round.			Square.		Hexagon.	
	Weight Per Inch.	Area Square Inches.	Circumference Inches.	Weight Per Inch.	Area Square Inches.	Weight Per Inch.	Area Square Inches.
1 13/16	.7317	2.5802	5.6941	.9316	3.2852	.8069	2.8450
1 7/8	.7831	2.7612	5.8905	.9970	3.5156	.8635	3.0446
1 15/16	.8361	2.9483	6.0868	1.0646	3.7539	.9220	3.2509
2	.8910	3.1416	6.2832	1.1342	4.0000	.9825	3.4573
2 1/16	.9475	3.3410	6.4795	1.2064	4.2539	1.0448	3.6840
2 1/8	1.0058	3.5466	6.6759	1.2806	4.5156	1.1091	3.9106
2 3/16	1.0658	3.7583	6.8722	1.3570	4.7852	1.1753	4.1440
2 1/4	1.1276	3.9761	7.0686	1.4357	5.0625	1.2434	4.3892
2 5/16	1.1911	4.2000	7.2649	1.5165	5.3477	1.3135	4.6312
2 3/8	1.2564	4.4301	7.4613	1.6569	5.6406	1.3854	4.8849
2 7/16	1.3234	4.6664	7.6575	1.6849	5.9414	1.4593	5.1454
2 1/2	1.3921	4.9087	7.8540	1.7724	6.2500	1.5351	5.4126
2 5/8	1.5348	5.4119	8.2467	1.9541	6.8906	1.6924	5.9674
2 3/4	1.6845	5.9396	8.6394	2.1446	7.5625	1.8574	6.5493
2 7/8	1.8411	6.4918	9.0321	2.3441	8.2656	2.0304	7.1590
3	2.0046	7.0686	9.4248	2.5548	9.0000	2.2105	7.7941
3 1/8	2.1752	7.6699	9.8175	2.7719	9.7656	2.3986	8.4573
3 1/4	2.3527	8.2958	10.2102	2.9954	10.5625	2.5918	9.1387
3 3/8	2.5371	8.9462	10.6029	3.2303	11.3906	2.7977	9.8646
3 1/2	2.7286	9.6211	10.9956	3.4740	12.2500	3.0083	10.6089
3 5/8	2.9269	10.3206	11.3883	3.7265	13.1407	3.2275	11.3798
3 3/4	3.1323	11.0447	11.7810	3.9880	14.0625	3.4539	12.1785
3 7/8	3.3446	11.7932	12.1737	4.2582	15.0156	3.6880	13.0035
4	3.5638	12.5664	12.5664	4.5374	16.0000	3.9298	13.8292
4 1/8	3.7900	13.3640	12.9591	4.8254	17.0156	4.1792	14.7359
4 1/4	4.0232	14.1863	13.3518	5.1223	18.0625	4.4364	15.6424
4 3/8	4.2634	15.0332	13.7445	5.4280	19.1406	4.7011	16.5761
4 1/2	4.5105	15.9043	14.1372	5.7426	20.2500	4.9736	17.5569
4 5/8	4.7645	16.8002	14.5299	6.0662	21.3906	5.2538	18.5249
4 3/4	5.0255	17.7205	14.9226	6.6276	22.5625	5.5416	19.5397
4 7/8	5.2935	18.6655	15.3153	6.7397	23.7656	5.8371	20.5816
5	5.5685	19.6350	15.7080	7.0897	25.0000	6.1403	21.6503
5 1/8	5.8504	20.6290	16.1007	7.4496	26.2656	6.4511	22.7456
5 1/4	6.1392	21.6475	16.4934	7.8164	27.5624	6.7697	23.8696
5 3/8	6.4351	22.6905	16.8861	8.1930	28.8906	7.0959	25.0198
5 1/2	6.7379	23.7583	17.2788	8.5786	30.2500	7.4298	26.1971
5 5/8	7.0476	24.8505	17.6715	8.9729	31.6406	7.7713	27.4013
5 3/4	7.3643	25.9672	18.0642	9.3762	33.0625	8.1214	28.6361
5 7/8	7.6880	27.1085	18.4569	9.7883	34.5156	8.4774	29.8913
6	8.0186	28.2743	18.8496	10.2192	36.0000	8.8420	31.1765
6 1/4	8.7007	30.6796	19.6350	11.0877	39.0625	9.5943	33.8291
6 1/2	9.4107	33.1831	20.4204	11.9817	42.2500	10.3673	36.5547
6 3/4	10.1485	35.7847	21.2058	12.9211	45.5625	11.1908	39.4584
7	10.9142	38.4845	21.9912	13.8960	49.0000	12.0351	42.4354
7 1/2	12.5291	44.1786	23.5620	15.9520	56.2500	13.8158	48.7142
8	14.2553	50.2655	25.1328	18.1497	64.0000	15.7192	55.3169

Multiply above weights by .993 for wrought iron, .918 for cast iron, 1.0331 for cast brass, 1.1209 for copper, and 1.1748 for phos. bronze.

WEIGHT OF IRON AND STEEL SHEETS.

Weights per Square Foot.—*Kent.*

Thickness by Birmingham Gauge.				Thickness by American (Brown and Sharpe's) Gauge.			
No. of Gauge.	Thickness in Inches.	Iron.	Stëel.	No. of Gauge.	Thickness in Inches.	Iron.	Steel.
0000	.454	18.16	18.52	0000	.46	18.40	18.77
000	.425	17.00	17.34	000	.4096	16.38	16.71
00	.38	15.20	15.50	00	.3648	14.59	14.88
0	.34	13.60	13.87	0	.3249	13.00	13.26
1	.3	12.00	12.24	1	.2893	11.57	11.80
2	.284	11.36	11.59	2	.2576	10.30	10.51
3	.259	10.36	10.57	3	.2294	9.18	9.36
4	.238	9.52	9.71	4	.2043	8.17	8.34
5	.22	8.80	8.98	5	.1819	7.28	7.42
6	.203	8.12	8.28	6	.1620	6.48	6.61
7	.18	7.20	7.34	7	.1443	5.77	5.89
8	.165	6.60	6.73	8	.1285	5.14	5.24
9	.148	5.92	6.04	9	.1144	4.58	4.67
10	.134	5.36	5.47	10	.1019	4.08	4.16
11	.12	4.80	4.90	11	.0907	3.63	3.70
12	.109	4.36	4.45	12	.0808	3.23	3.30
13	.095	3.80	3.88	13	.0720	2.88	2.94
14	.083	3.32	3.39	14	.0641	2.56	2.62
15	.072	2.88	2.94	15	.0571	2.28	2.33
16	.065	2.60	2.65	16	.0508	2.03	2.07
17	.058	2.32	2.37	17	.0453	1.81	1.85
18	.049	1.96	2.00	18	.0403	1.61	1.64
19	.042	1.68	1.71	19	.0359	1.44	1.46
20	.035	1.40	1.43	20	.0320	1.28	1.31
21	.032	1.28	1.31	21	.0285	1.14	1.16
22	.028	1.12	1.14	22	.0253	1.01	1.03
23	.025	1.00	1.02	23	.0226	.904	.922
24	.022	.88	.898	24	.0201	.804	.820
25	.02	.80	.816	25	.0179	.716	.730
26	.018	.72	.734	26	.0159	.636	.649
27	.016	.64	.653	27	.0142	.568	.579
28	.014	.56	.571	28	.0126	.504	.514
29	.013	.52	.530	29	.0113	.452	.461
30	.012	.48	.490	30	.0100	.400	.408
31	.01	.40	.408	31	.0089	.356	.363
32	.009	.36	.367	32	.0080	.320	.326
33	.008	.32	.326	33	.0071	.284	.290
34	.007	.28	.286	34	.0063	.252	.257
35	.005	.20	.204	35	.0056	.224	.228

	Iron.	Steel
Specific gravity	7.7	7.854
Weight per cubic foot........	480.	489.6
Weight per cubic inch........	.2778	.2833

As there are many gauges in use differing from each other, and even the thicknesses of a certain specified gauge, as the Birmingham, are not assumed the same by all manufacturers, orders for sheets and wires should always state the weights per square foot, or the thickness in thousandths of an inch.

WEIGHTS OF SQUARE AND ROUND BARS OF WROUGHT IRON IN POUNDS PER LINEAL FOOT.—*Kent.*

Iron weighing 480 lbs. per cubic foot.

For steel add 2 per cent.

Thickness or Diameter in Inches	Weight of Square Bar One Foot Long.	Weight of Round Bar One Foot Long.	Thickness or Diameter in Inches.	Weight of Square Bar One Foot Long.	Weight of Round Bar One Foot Long.
0			2 11-16	24.08	18.91
1-16	.013	.010	3-4	25.21	19.80
1-8	.052	.041	13-16	26.37	20.71
3 16	.117	.092	7-8	27.55	21.64
1-4	.208	.164	15-16	28.76	22.59
5-16	.326	.256	3	30.00	23.56
3-8	.469	.368	1-16	31.26	24.55
7-16	.638	.501	1-8	32.55	25.57
1-2	.833	.654	3-16	33.87	26.60
9-16	1.055	.828	1-4	35.21	27.65
5-8	1.302	1.023	5-16	36.58	28.73
11-16	1.576	1.237	3-8	37.97	29.82
3-4	1.875	1.473	7-16	39.39	30.94
13-16	2.201	1.728	1-2	40.83	32.07
7-8	2.552	2.004	9-16	42.30	33.23
15-16	2.930	2.301	5-8	43.80	34.40
1	3.333	2.618	11-16	45.33	35.60
1-16	3.763	2.955	3-4	46.88	36.82
1-8	4.219	3.313	13-16	48.45	38.05
3-16	4.701	3.692	7-8	50.05	39.31
1-4	5.208	4.091	15-16	51.68	40.59
5-16	5.742	4.510	4	53.33	41.89
3-8	6.302	4.950	1-16	55.01	43.21
7-16	6.888	5.410	1-8	56.72	44.55
1-2	7.500	5.890	3-16	58.45	45.91
9-16	8.138	6.392	1-4	60.21	47.29
5-8	8.802	6.913	5-16	61.99	48.69
11-16	9.492	7.455	3-8	63.80	50.11
3-4	10.21	8.018	7-16	65.64	51.55
13-16	10.95	8.601	1-2	67.50	53.01
7-8	11.72	9.204	9-16	69.39	54.50
15-16	12.51	9.828	5-8	71.30	56.00
2	13.33	10.47	11-16	73.24	57.52
1-16	14.18	11.14	3-4	75.21	59.07
1-8	15.05	11.82	13-16	77.20	60.63
3-16	15.95	12.53	7-8	79.22	62.22
1-4	16.88	13.25	15-16	81.26	63.82
5-16	17.83	14.00	5	83.33	65.45
3-8	18.80	14.77	1-16	85.43	67.10
7-16	19.80	15.55	1-8	87.55	68.76
1-2	20.83	16.36	3-16	89.70	70.45
9-16	21.89	17.19	1-4	91.88	72.16
5-8	22.97	18.04	5-16	94.08	73.89

WEIGHTS OF SQUARE AND ROUND BARS OF WROUGHT IRON IN
POUNDS PER LINEAL FOOT.—*Kent.*

Iron weighing 480 lbs. per cubic foot.

For steel add 2 per cent.

Thickness or Diameter in Inches.	Weight of Square Bar One Foot Long.	Weight of Round Bar One Foot Long.	Thickness or Diameter in Inches.	Weight of Square Bar One Foot Long.	Weight of Round Bar One Foot Long.
5 3-8	96.30	75.64	7 1-2	187.5	147.3
7-16	98.55	77.40	5-8	193.8	152.2
1-2	100.8	79.19	3-4	200.2	157.2
9-16	103.1	81.00	7-8	206.7	162.4
5-8	105.5	82.83	8	213.3	167.6
11-16	107.8	84.69	1-4	226.9	178.2
3-4	110.2	86.56	1-2	240.8	189.2
13-16	112.6	88.45	3-4	255.2	200.4
7-8	115.1	90.36	9	270.0	212.1
15-16	117.5	92.29	1-4	285.2	224.0
6	120.0	94.25	1-2	300.8	236.3
1-8	125.1	98.22	3-4	316.9	248.9
1-4	130.2	102.3	10	333.3	261.8
3-8	135.5	106.4	1-4	350.2	275.1
1-2	140.8	110.6	1-2	367.5	288.6
5-8	146.3	114.9	3-4	385.2	302.5
3-4	151.9	119.3	11	403.3	316.8
7-8	157.6	123.7	1-4	421.9	331.3
7	163.3	128.3	1-2	440.8	346.2
1-8	169.2	132.9	3-4	460.2	361.4
1-4	175.2	137.6	12	480.	377.
3-8	181.3	142.4			

To compute the Weight of Sheet Steel:

Divide the thickness, expressed in thousandths, by 25;
the result is the weight, in pounds, per square foot.

UNITED STATES WEIGHTS AND MEASURES.

Measures of Length.

12 inches.................... 1 foot.
3 feet.......................1 yard.
5½ yards or 16½ feet........ 1 rod.
40 rods or 220 yards........ 1 furlong.
8 furlongs, or 1760 yds., or 5,280 ft. 1 mile.

Measures of Surface.

144 square inches............1 square foot.
9 square feet..............1 square yard.
30¼ sq. yds., or 272¼ sq. ft..1 square rod.
160 sq. rods, or 4840 sq. yards 1 acre.
640 acres.................... 1 square mile.

Measures of Volume.

1728 cubic inches............ 1 cubic foot.
27 cubic feet...............1 cubic yard.
128 cubic feet............... 1 cord wood.

Measures of Weight.

Commercial.

437½ grains (Troy)........ 1 ounce Avoirdupois.
16 ounces or 7000 grains ....1 pound (lb.) Avoirdupois.
100 pounds..................1 hundredweight (cwt.)
20 hundredweight or 2000 lbs 1 net ton.
2240 pounds................ 1 gross ton.

TAP DRILLS FOR MACHINE SCREW TAPS.

These drills will give a thread full enough for all practical purposes, but not a *full* thread.

Sizes of Taps	No. of Threads	Sizes of Drills	Sizes of Taps	No. of Threads	Sizes of Drills
2	48	48	12	24	19
2	56	46	13	20	17
2	64	45	13	24	15
3	40	48	14	20	14
3	48	47	14	22	13
3	56	45	14	24	11
4	32	45	15	18	12
4	36	43	15	20	10
4	40	42	15	24	7
5	30	41	16	16	10
5	32	40	16	18	7
5	36	38	16	20	5
5	40	36	16	24	1
6	30	39	17	16	7
6	32	37	17	18	4
6	36	35	17	20	2
6	40	33	18	16	2
7	28	32	18	18	1
7	30	31	18	20	B
7	32	30	19	16	C
8	24	31	19	18	D
8	30	30	19	20	E
8	32	29	20	16	E
9	24	29	20	18	E
9	28	27	20	20	F
9	30	26	22	16	H
9	32	24	22	18	I
10	24	26	24	14	K
10	28	24	24	16	L
10	30	23	24	18	M
10	32	21	26	14	O
11	24	20	26	16	P
11	28	19	28	14	R
11	30	18	28	16	S
12	20	21	30	14	T
12	22	19	30	16	U

SIZE OF DRILLS FOR STANDARD PIPE TAPS.

Nom'l Diam.	Threads per inch	Diam. of Drill	Nom'l Diam.	Threads per inch	Diam of Drill	Nom'l Diam.	Threads per inch	Diam. of Drill
1/8	27	21/64	1	11 1/2	1 3/16	3	8	3 1/4
1/4	18	27/64	1 1/4	11 1/2	1 15/32	3 1/2	8	3 3/4
3/8	18	19/32	1 1/2	11 1/2	1 23/32	4	8	4 1/4
1/2	14	23/32	2	11 1/2	2 3/16	4 1/2	8	4 3/4
3/4	14	15/16	2 1/2	8	2 5/8	5	8	5 1/16

DIFFERENT STANDARDS FOR WIRE GAGE IN USE IN THE UNITED
STATES.

Dimensions of Sizes in Decimal Parts of an Inch

Number of Wire Gauge.	American or Brown & Sharpe.	Birmingham, or Stubs' Wire.	Washburn & Moen Mfg Co., Worcester,Ms.	Imperial Wire Gauge	Stubs' Steel Wire.	U. S. Stand. for Plate.	Number of Wire Gauge.
000000	....	....	....	.464	...	.46875	000000
00000	....	....	....	.432	....	.4375	00000
0000	.46	.454	.3938	.400	....	.40625	0000
000	.40964	.425	.3625	.372	....	.375	000
00	.3648	.38	.3310	.348	....	.34375	00
0	.32486	.34	.3065	.324	....	.3125	0
1	.2893	.3	.2830	.300	.227	.28125	1
2	.25763	.284	.2625	.276	.219	.265625	2
3	.22942	.259	.2437	.252	.212	.25	3
4	.20431	.238	.2253	.232	.207	.234375	4
5	.18194	.22	.2070	.212	.204	.21875	5
6	.16202	.203	.1920	.192	.201	.203125	6
7	.14428	.18	.1770	.176	.199	.1875	7
8	.12849	.165	.1620	.160	.197	.171875	8
9	.11443	.148	.1483	.144	.194	.15625	9
10	.10189	.134	.1350	.128	.191	.140625	10
11	.090742	.12	.1205	.116	.188	.125	11
12	.080808	.109	.1055	104	.185	.109375	12
13	.071961	.095	.0915	.092	.182	.09375	13
14	.064084	.083	.0800	.080	.180	.078125	14
15	.057068	.072	.0720	.072	.178	.0708125	15
16	05082	.065	.0625	.064	.175	.0625	16
17	.045257	.058	.0540	.056	.172	.05625	17
18	.040303	.049	.0475	.048	.168	.05	18
19	.03589	.042	.0410	.040	.164	.04375	19
20	.031961	.035	.0348	.036	.161	.0375	20
21	.028462	,032	.03175	.032	.157	.034375	21
22	.025347	.028	.0286	.028	.155	.03125	22
23	.022571	.025	.0258	.024	.153	028125	23
24	.0201	.022	.0230	.022	.151	.025	24
25	.0179	.02	.0204	.020	.148	.021875	25
26	.01594	.018	.0181	.018	.146	.01875	26
27	.014195	.016	.0173	.0164	.143	.0171875	27
28	.012641	.014	.0162	.0149	.139	.015625	28
29	.011257	.013	.0150	.0136	.134	.0140625	29
30	.010025	.012	.0140	.0124	.127	.0125	30
31	.008928	.01	.0132	.0116	.120	.0109375	31
32	.00795	.009	.0128	.0108	.115	.01015625	32
33	.00708	.008	.0118	.0100	.112	.009375	33
34	.006304	.007	.0104	.0092	.110	.00859375	34
35	.005614	.005	.0095	.0084	.108	.0078125	35
36	.005	.004	.0090	.0076	.106	.00703125	36
37	.004453	....	....	.0068	.103	.006640625	37
38	.003965	....	....	.0060	.101	.00625	38
39	.003531	....	....	.0052	.099	....	39
40	.003144	....	....	.0048	.097	....	40

U. S. STANDARD SCREW THREADS.

Diameter of Screw.	Threads to Inch.	Diameter at Root of Thread.	Width of Flat.
¼	20	.185	.0063
5⁄16	18	.2403	.0069
⅜	16	.2936	.0078
7⁄16	14	.3447	.0089
½	13	.4001	.0096
9⁄16	12	.4542	.0104
⅝	11	.5069	.0114
¾	10	.6201	.0125
⅞	9	.7307	.0139
1	8	.8376	.0156
1⅛	7	.9394	.0179
1¼	7	1.0644	.0179
1⅜	6	1.1585	.0208
1½	6	1.2835	.0208
1⅝	5½	1.3888	.0227
1¾	5	1.4902	.0250
1⅞	5	1.6152	.0250
2	4½	1.7113	.0278
2¼	4½	1.9613	.0278
2½	4	2.1752	.0313
2¾	4	2.4252	.0313
3	3½	2.6288	.0357
3¼	3½	2.8788	.0357
3½	3¼	3.1003	.0385
3¾	3	3.3170	.0417
4	3	3.5670	.0417
4¼	2⅞	3.7982	.0435
4½	2¾	4.0276	.0455
4¾	2⅝	4.2551	.0476
5	2½	4.4804	.0500
5¼	2½	4.7304	.0500
5½	2⅜	4.9530	.0526
5¾	2⅜	5.2030	.0526
6	2¼	5.4226	.0556

SHARP " V " THREAD.

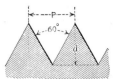

Formula :

$$p = \text{pitch} = \frac{1}{\text{No. threads per inch}}$$

$$d = \text{depth} = p \times .8660.$$

Diameter	$\frac{1}{4}$	$\frac{5}{16}$	$\frac{3}{8}$	$\frac{7}{16}$	$\frac{1}{2}$	$\frac{9}{16}$	$\frac{5}{8}$	$\frac{11}{16}$	$\frac{3}{4}$	$\frac{13}{16}$
No. Threads per inch.	20	18	16	14	12	12	11	11	10	10
Diameter	$\frac{7}{8}$	$\frac{15}{16}$	1	$1\frac{1}{8}$	$1\frac{1}{4}$	$1\frac{3}{8}$	$1\frac{1}{2}$	$1\frac{5}{8}$	$1\frac{3}{4}$	$1\frac{7}{8}$
No. Threads per inch.	9	9	8	7	7	6	6	5	5	$4\frac{1}{2}$
Diameter	2	$2\frac{1}{8}$	$2\frac{1}{4}$	$2\frac{3}{8}$	$2\frac{1}{2}$	$2\frac{5}{8}$	$2\frac{3}{4}$	$2\frac{7}{8}$	3	$3\frac{1}{8}$
No. Threads per inch.	$4\frac{1}{2}$	$4\frac{1}{2}$	$4\frac{1}{2}$	$4\frac{1}{2}$	4	4	4	4	$3\frac{1}{2}$	$3\frac{1}{2}$
Diameter	$3\frac{1}{4}$	$3\frac{3}{8}$	$3\frac{1}{2}$	$3\frac{5}{8}$	$3\frac{3}{4}$	$3\frac{7}{8}$	4			
No. Threads per inch.	$3\frac{1}{2}$	$3\frac{1}{4}$	$3\frac{1}{4}$	$3\frac{1}{4}$	3	3	3			

UNITED STATES STANDARD THREAD.

Formula :

$$p = \text{pitch} = \frac{1}{\text{No. threads per inch}}$$

$$d = \text{depth} = p \times .6495.$$

$$f = \text{flat} = \frac{p}{8}$$

Diameter	$\frac{1}{4}$	$\frac{5}{16}$	$\frac{3}{8}$	$\frac{7}{16}$	$\frac{1}{2}$	$\frac{9}{16}$	$\frac{5}{8}$	$\frac{3}{4}$	$\frac{7}{8}$
No. Threads per inch.	20	18	16	14	13	12	11	10	9
Diameter	1	$1\frac{1}{8}$	$1\frac{1}{4}$	$1\frac{3}{8}$	$1\frac{1}{2}$	$1\frac{5}{8}$	$1\frac{3}{4}$	$1\frac{7}{8}$	2
No. Threads per inch.	8	7	7	6	6	$5\frac{1}{2}$	5	5	$4\frac{1}{2}$
Diameter	$2\frac{1}{8}$	$2\frac{1}{4}$	$2\frac{3}{8}$	$2\frac{1}{2}$	$2\frac{5}{8}$	$2\frac{3}{4}$	$2\frac{7}{8}$	3	$3\frac{1}{8}$
No. Threads per inch.	$4\frac{1}{2}$	$4\frac{1}{2}$	4	4	4	4	$3\frac{1}{2}$	$3\frac{1}{2}$	$3\frac{1}{2}$
Diameter	$3\frac{1}{4}$	$3\frac{3}{8}$	$3\frac{1}{2}$	$3\frac{5}{8}$	$3\frac{3}{4}$	$3\frac{7}{8}$	4		
No. Threads per inch.	$3\frac{1}{2}$	$3\frac{1}{4}$	$3\frac{1}{4}$	$3\frac{1}{4}$	3	3	3		

WHITWORTH STANDARD THREAD.

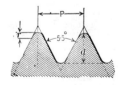

Formula :

$$p = \text{pitch} = \frac{1}{\text{No. threads per inch}}$$

$$d = \text{depth} = p \times .64033.$$

$$r = \text{radius} = p \times .1373.$$

Diameter	$\frac{1}{4}$	$\frac{5}{16}$	$\frac{3}{8}$	$\frac{7}{16}$	$\frac{1}{2}$	$\frac{9}{16}$	$\frac{5}{8}$	$\frac{11}{16}$	$\frac{3}{4}$	$\frac{13}{16}$
No. Threads per inch.	20	18	16	14	12	12	11	11	10	10
Diameter	$\frac{7}{8}$	$\frac{15}{16}$	1	$1\frac{1}{8}$	$1\frac{1}{4}$	$1\frac{3}{8}$	$1\frac{1}{2}$	$1\frac{5}{8}$	$1\frac{3}{4}$	$1\frac{7}{8}$
No. Threads per inch.	9	9	8	7	7	6	6	5	5	$4\frac{1}{2}$
Diameter	2	$2\frac{1}{8}$	$2\frac{1}{4}$	$2\frac{3}{8}$	$2\frac{1}{2}$	$2\frac{5}{8}$	$2\frac{3}{4}$	$2\frac{7}{8}$	3	$3\frac{1}{8}$
No. Threads per inch.	$4\frac{1}{2}$	$4\frac{1}{2}$	4	4	4	4	$3\frac{1}{2}$	$3\frac{1}{2}$	$3\frac{1}{2}$	$3\frac{1}{2}$
Diameter	$3\frac{1}{4}$	$3\frac{3}{8}$	$3\frac{1}{2}$	$3\frac{5}{8}$	$3\frac{3}{4}$	$3\frac{7}{8}$	4			
No. Threads per inch.	$3\frac{1}{4}$	$3\frac{1}{4}$	$3\frac{1}{4}$	$3\frac{1}{4}$	3	3	3			

THE ACME STANDARD THREAD.

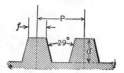

The Acme Standard Thread is an adaptation of the most commonly used style of Worm Thread and is intended to take the place of the square thread.

It is a little shallower than the Worm Thread, but the same depth as the square thread and much stronger than the latter.

The various parts of the Acme Standard Thread are obtained as follows:

Width of Point of tool for Screw or Tap Thread

$$= \frac{.3707}{\text{No. of Thds. per in.}} - .0052$$

$$\text{Width of Screw or Nut Thread} = \frac{.3707}{\text{No. of Thds. per in.}}$$

Diameter of Tap = Diameter of Screw + .020.

Diameter of Tap or Screw at Root =

$$\text{Diameter of Screw} - \left(\frac{1}{\text{No. of Linear Thds. per in.}} + .020 \right)$$

$$\text{Depth of thread} = \frac{1}{2 \times \text{No. of Thds. per in.}} + .010$$

TABLE OF THREAD PARTS.

No. of Threads per inch.	Depth of Thread.	Width at Top of Thread.	Width at Bottom of Thread.	Space at Top of Thread.	Thickness at Root of Thread.
1	.5100	.3707	.3655	.6293	.6345
1⅓	.3850	.2780	.2728	.4720	.4772
2	.2600	.1853	.1801	.3147	.3199
3	.1767	.1235	.1183	.2098	.2150
4	.1350	.0927	.0875	.1573	.1625
5	.1100	.0741	.0689	.1259	.1311
6	.0933	.0618	.0566	.1049	.1101
7	.0814	.0529	.0478	.0899	.0951
8	.0725	.0463	.0411	.0787	.0839
9	.0655	.0413	.0361	.0699	.0751
10	.0600	.0371	.0319	.0629	.0681

AVERAGE CUTTING SPEED FOR DRILLS.

The following table represents the most approved practice in rate of cutting speed for drills ranging from 1-16 inch to 3 inches in diameter.

Diam. of Drills	Speed on C. Iron	Speed on Steel	Diam. of Drills	Speed on C. Iron	Speed on Steel
$\frac{1}{16}$	2,289	1,704	$1\frac{9}{16}$	71	46
$\frac{1}{8}$	1,134	840	$1\frac{5}{8}$	67	43
$\frac{3}{16}$	749	553	$1\frac{11}{16}$	64	41
$\frac{1}{4}$	556	409	$1\frac{3}{4}$	61	39
$\frac{5}{16}$	441	322	$1\frac{13}{16}$	58	37
$\frac{3}{8}$	363	265	$1\frac{7}{8}$	56	35
$\frac{7}{16}$	309	224	$1\frac{15}{16}$	53	33
$\frac{1}{2}$	267	193	2	51	31
$\frac{9}{16}$	235	169	$2\frac{1}{16}$	49	29
$\frac{5}{8}$	210	150	$2\frac{1}{8}$	47	28
$\frac{11}{16}$	189	134	$2\frac{3}{16}$	45	26
$\frac{3}{4}$	171	121	$2\frac{1}{4}$	43	25
$1\frac{3}{16}$	156	110	$2\frac{5}{16}$	41	24
$\frac{7}{8}$	144	100	$2\frac{3}{8}$	39	23
$1\frac{15}{16}$	133	92	$2\frac{7}{16}$	38	21
1	123	85	$2\frac{1}{2}$	36	20
$1\frac{1}{16}$	114	79	$2\frac{9}{16}$	35	19
$1\frac{1}{8}$	107	73	$2\frac{5}{8}$	34	18
$1\frac{3}{16}$	100	68	$2\frac{11}{16}$	32	17
$1\frac{1}{4}$	94	68	$2\frac{3}{4}$	31	16
$1\frac{5}{16}$	89	59	$2\frac{13}{16}$	30	15
$1\frac{3}{8}$	83	56	$2\frac{7}{8}$	29	15
$1\frac{7}{16}$	79	52	$2\frac{15}{16}$	28	14
$1\frac{1}{2}$	75	49	3	27	13

TABLE OF CUTTING SPEEDS.

Feet per Minute.	5′	10′	15′	20′	25′	30′	35′	40′	45′	50′
Diam.	REVOLUTIONS PER MINUTE.									
½	38.2	76.4	114 6	152.9	191.1	229.3	267.5	305.7	344.0	382.2
⅝	30.6	61.2	91.8	122.5	153.1	183.7	214.3	244.9	275.5	306.1
¾	25.4	50.8	76.3	101.7	127.1	152.5	178.0	203.4	228.8	254.2
⅞	21.8	43.6	65.5	87.3	109.1	130.9	152.7	174.5	196.3	218.9
1	19.1	38.2	57.3	76.4	95.5	114.6	133.8	152.9	172.0	191.1
1⅛	17.0	34.0	51.0	68.0	85.6	102.0	119.0	136.0	153.0	170.0
1¼	15.3	30.6	45.8	61.2	76.3	91.8	106.9	122.5	137.4	153.1
1⅜	13.9	27.8	41.7	55.6	69.5	83.3	97.2	111.1	125.0	138.9
1½	12.7	25.4	38.2	50.8	63.7	76.3	89.2	101.7	114.6	127.1
1⅝	11.8	23.5	35.0	47.0	58.8	70.5	82.2	93.9	105.7	117.4
1¾	10.9	21.8	32.7	43.6	54.5	65.5	76.4	87 3	98.2	109.1
1⅞	10.2	20.4	30.6	40.7	50.9	61.1	71.3	81.5	91.9	101.9
2	9.6	19.1	28.7	38.2	47.8	57.3	66.9	76.4	86.0	95.5
2¼	8.5	17.0	25.4	34.0	42.4	51.0	59.4	68.0	76.2	85.0
2½	7.6	15.3	22.9	30.6	38.2	45.8	53.5	61.2	68.8	76.3
2¾	6.9	13 9	20.8	27.8	34.7	41.7	48.6	55.6	62.5	69.5
3	6.4	12.7	19.1	25.5	31.8	38.2	44.6	51.0	57.3	63.7
3½	5.5	10.9	16.4	21.8	27.3	32.7	38.2	43.6	49.1	54.5
4	4.8	9.6	14.3	19.1	23.9	28.7	33.4	38 2	43.0	47.8
4½	4.2	8.5	12.7	16.9	21.2	25.4	29.6	34.0	38 1	42.4
5	3.8	7.6	11.5	15.3	19.1	22.9	26.7	30.6	34.4	38.2
5½	3.5	6.9	10.4	13.9	17.4	20.8	24.3	27.8	31.3	34.7
6	3.2	6.4	9.6	12.7	15.9	19.1	22.3	25.5	28.7	31.8
7	2.7	5.5	8.1	10.9	13.6	16.4	19.1	21.8	24.6	27.3
8	2.4	4.8	7.2	9.6	11.9	14.3	16.7	19 1	21.1	23.9
9	2.1	4.2	6.4	8.5	10.6	12.7	14.9	17.0	19.1	21.2
10	1.9	3.8	5.7	7.6	9.6	11.5	13.4	15 3	17.2	19.1
11	1.7	3.5	5.2	6.9	8.7	10.4	12.2	13.9	15.6	17.4
12	1.6	3.2	4.8	6.4	8.0	9.6	11.1	12.7	14.3	15.9
13	1.5	2.9	4.4	5.9	7.3	8.8	10.3	11.8	13.2	14.7
14	1.4	2.7	4.1	5.5	6.8	8.1	9.6	10.9	12.3	13.6
15	1.3	2.5	3.8	5.1	6.4	7.6	8.9	10.2	11.5	12.7
16	1.2	2.4	3.6	4.8	6.0	7.2	8.4	9.6	10.7	11.9
17	1.1	2.2	3.4	4.5	5.6	6.7	7.9	9.0	10.1	11.2
18	1.1	2.1	3.2	4.2	5.3	6.4	7.4	8.5	9.6	10.6
19	1.0	2.0	3.0	4.0	5.0	6.0	7.0	8.0	9.1	10.1
20	1.0	1.9	2.9	3.8	4.8	5.7	6.7	7.6	8.6	9.6
21	.9	1.8	2.7	3.6	4.5	5.5	6.4	7.3	8.1	9.1
22	.9	1.7	2.6	3.5	4.3	5.2	6.1	6.9	7.8	8.7
23	.8	1.7	2.5	3.3	4.1	5.0	5.8	6.6	7.5	8.3
24	.8	1.6	2.4	3.2	4.0	4.8	5.6	6.4	7.2	8.0
25	.8	1.5	2.3	3 1	3.8	4.6	5.3	6.1	6.9	7.6
26	.7	1.5	2.2	2.9	3.7	4.4	5.1	5.9	6.6	7.3
27	.7	1.4	2.1	2.8	3.5	4.2	5.0	5.7	6.4	7.1
28	.7	1.4	2.0	2.7	3.4	4.1	4.8	5.5	6.1	6.8
29	.7	1.3	2.0	2.6	3.3	4.0	4.6	5.3	5.9	6.6
30	.6	1.3	1.9	2.5	3.2	3.8	4.5	5.1	5.7	6.4

The preceding table is a convenient one for finding the number of revolutions per minute required to give a periphery speed from 5 to 50 feet per minute of diameters from ½ inch to 30 inches.

EXAMPLES—A mill 2 inches diam. to have a periphery speed of 35 feet per minute, should make about 67 revolutions, while a 1⅛-inch mill should make 120 revolutions to have the same periphery speed. If a ¾-inch mill makes 250 revolutions per minute, the periphery speed is about 50 feet.

Horse Power of Belts.—A good method of finding the power of a belt, assuming 800 feet travel per minute of 1 inch single belt per horse power.

FORMULA—.00033 D. R. B = Horse power.

D = Diameter of pulley in inches.
R = Revolutions of pulley per minute.
B = Width of belt in inches.

EXAMPLE—18-inch pulley, 3-inch belt, 150 revolutions per minute, .00033 x 18 x 150 x 3 = 2.67 H. P.

If 1000 feet is assumed instead of 800 feet, use constant .00026 in place of .00033.

CUTTER LUBRICANT.

A good lubricant for cutters milling steel or wrought iron, is 1 lb. tallow or 1 lb. hard or soft soap. Boil and add water until about the consistency of cream.

CHAPTER XII.

Cutter and Tool Grinding.

A subject germain to the treatment of steel is that of grinding, as in most lines of steel working it occupies an important position. In the following are shown illustrations of approved machines for the grinding of fine tool work and accurate small machine parts. Descriptions are also given of the correct methods of grinding the different tools and parts.

The machine illustrated in Fig. 146 is of a type used extensively for general toolroom work and is one of a class of universal cutter and tool grinders which has been greatly improved and developed during the last few years. It may be used to grind accurately and rapidly work of the following kinds and sizes:

Milling machine cutters 12 inches in diameter when not more than 1 inch wide.

Work 14 inches long held between centers when the diameter of rotation is not more than 8 inches. These dimensions are given as the limit for irregular pieces and not for heavy, solid cylinders.

Work 14 inches long can be ground by using an emery wheel on each side of the head.

Reamers and shell counterbores of large or small sizes.

Gear cutters and formed cutters of every description.

Flat surfaces, such as shear plates, dies and gages.

Hardened bushing and other pieces to be ground internally.

Conical surfaces, such as taper bearings and mandrels, and small cylindrical machine parts which are to be finished with extreme accuracy.

The foregoing list does not give the limit of the capacity of machine, but rather indicates in a general way what is possible in its use.

For a more particular presentation of the kinds of work which can be and are actually ground on such machines, reference is made to the following pages.

Prominent Features.

Those familiar with grinding the side teeth of side milling and angular cutters are aware that the tooth rest must be set to the exact height so as to bring the cutting edge of the tooth to be ground in an exact parallel line with the slide. In some machines

FIG. 146.—CINCINNATI UNIVERSAL CUTTER AND TOOL GRINDER.

this adjustment of the tooth rest for this grinding is complicated. The difficulty, however, is overcome in this machine, as no attention is required to adjust the tooth rest, since it is centrally fixed for all diameters of cutters. The tooth rest travels with the cutter, except in the grinding of spiral mills and large saws.

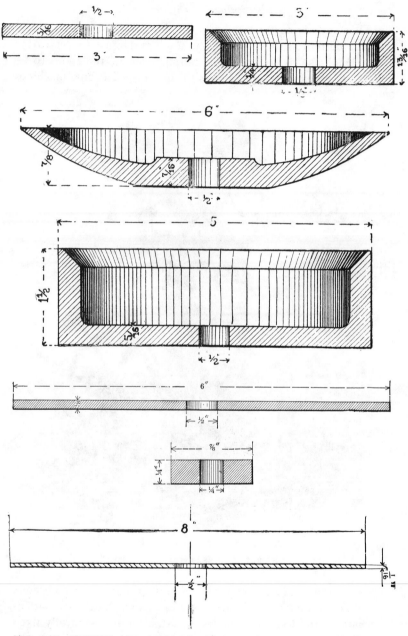

FIG. 147.—SHAPES AND SIZES OF EMERY WHEELS TO USE FOR TOOL GRINDING.

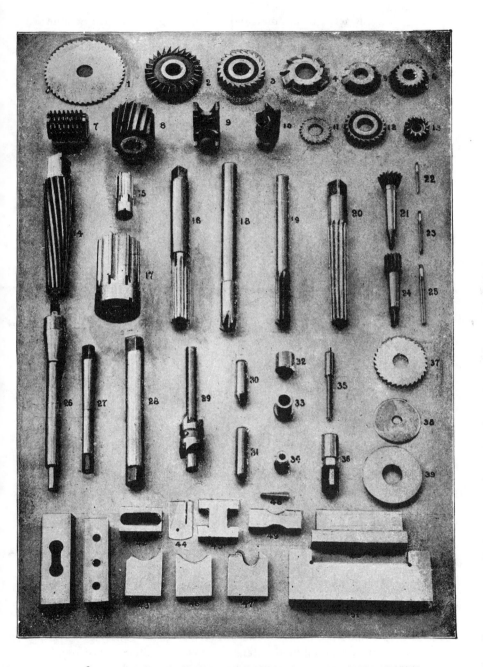

FIG. 148.—SAMPLES OF GROUND WORK DONE IN UNIVERSAL CUTTER
AND TOOL GRINDER, FIG. 146.

The side teeth of angular and side milling cutters are ground off with practically a straight line clearance. This is done with a cup-shape emery wheel 3 inches in diameter on the left side of the machine. The advantages of grinding side teeth with a fair size emery wheel, and at the same time grinding a straight line clearance with an accompanying strong cutting edge, are known to those who have heretofore been compelled to use a small wheel grinding a hollow clearance and weak-cutting edge. (See Fig. 149.)

To prevent the drawing of the temper from cutting edges of side mills and the side teeth of angular cutters, etc., which have a

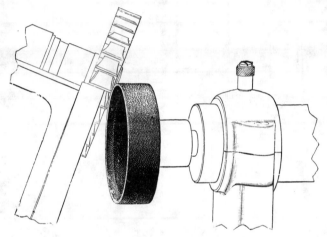

FIG. 149.—GRINDING SIDE TEETH.

broad surface, it is important that the heel of the tooth be stocked out first at a sharp angle, and only a small portion left to be ground at a different angle. The change from stocking out to the grinding of the cutting edge is quickly made by moving the knee a few degrees around the column.

This feature of revolving the knee around the column has also the following advantages:

Work can be brought in contact with the emery wheels on either side of the wheel without rechucking. Also the article to be ground can be brought in contact with the emery wheel in the most favorable position to either wheel for rapid grinding. For an example, a side milling cutter may have the outer teeth ground off on the straight face emery wheel on the right side of the machine, and the side teeth on the cup-shape wheel at the left side of the machine, without taking the cutter off the arbor or disturbing the tooth guide.

Cutters of small diameters and sharp angles can be ground without the cutter, mandrel or centers striking the belt or emery wheel head. Also in grinding the shoulders, on work revolved between centers, the periphery instead of the side of a flat wheel can be used.

Grinding a Spiral Mill.

Fig. 150 shows the long slide at the rear of the column and nearly parallel to the emery wheel spindle, the two swivels set at

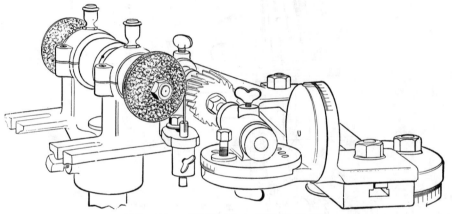

FIG. 150.—GRINDING A SPIRAL MILL.

zero, a flat wheel on the right of the emery wheel head and the mill on the mandrel held between centers.

Fig. 151 shows a side elevation of the wheel, the centering gage, the tooth rest No. 2 and the end of the mill.

Fig. 152 is an elevation showing the rim of the wheel, the face of the mill and the tooth rest in the position required when the mill is turned for grinding the next tooth.

Directions: Adjust the plane of centers below the plane of the spindle the distance required for clearance. If the mill is cylindrical, set the table at zero; and if not, set it for the required taper. Set the stops on the long slide so that, the mill having passed, the cutter will still be held by the flexible part of the tooth rest, which will then act as a spring pawl when turning the mill to bring the next tooth into position for grinding. In setting the tooth rest the centering gage must come directly opposite to part of the wheel which strikes the cutter.

Grinding Angular Cutters.

Fig. 153 illustrates the grinding when the cutter is left-hand.

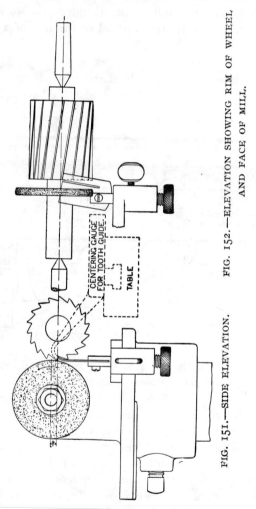

FIG. 152.—ELEVATION SHOWING RIM OF WHEEL, AND FACE OF MILL.

CENTERING GAUGE FOR TOOTH GUIDE.

TABLE

FIG. 151.—SIDE ELEVATION.

The flat wheel is on the right-hand end of spindle, the long slide is at the rear and right-hand, the cutter is held on work spindle and the tooth rest No. 4 is on the horizontal swivel.

Directions: Set the plane of centers below plane of spindle

the distance required for clearance. Set the long slide at a convenient angle, and then adjust the horizontal swivel to the angle required for the cutter.

Fig. 154 illustrates the grinding when the cutter is right-hand.

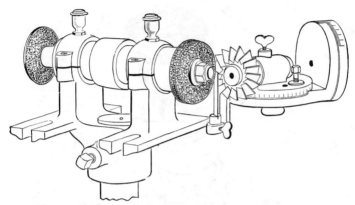

FIG. 153.—GRINDING A LEFT-HAND ANGULAR CUTTER.

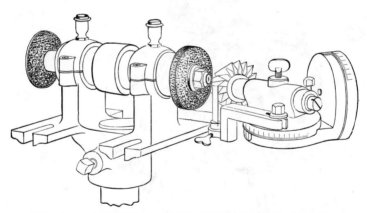

FIG. 154.—GRINDING A RIGHT-HAND ANGULAR CUTTER.

The explanations and directions for Fig. 153 are sufficient for Fig. 154.

Grinding Side Milling Cutters.

Fig. 155 shows the situation of the long slide at the back of the column, the cutter held by work spindle alone, the flat wheel on the right of the emery wheel head, and the tooth rest No. 3 fastened to the horizontal swivel.

Directions: Set the plane of centers the distance below the plane of the spindle required for clearance.

Fig. 156 shows the left-hand radial teeth in position for grinding, the 3-inch cup wheel on the left of the emery wheel head,

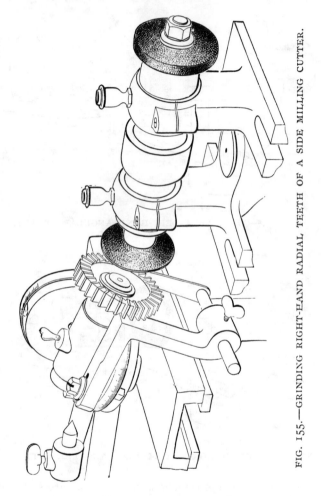

FIG. 155.—GRINDING RIGHT-HAND RADIAL TEETH OF A SIDE MILLING CUTTER.

the long slide on the left, the universal head on the end of the table and tooth rest No. 3 on the horizontal swivel.

It will be observed in the cuts that the side of the cutter opposite the one being ground is always closer to the emery wheel head than the other; that is, the index on the knee will point about 5 degrees beyond the 90 degree point.

Directions: Set the vertical swivel so as to depress the outer end of the work spindle the number of degrees required for clearance. This ranges from 5 degrees to 20 degrees, depending upon the clearance required.

The manner in which shell counterbores may be ground is

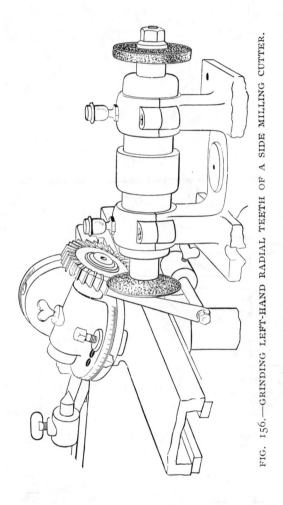

FIG. 156.—GRINDING LEFT-HAND RADIAL TEETH OF A SIDE MILLING CUTTER.

shown clearly in Fig. 157, and but little description is necessary. In grinding such tools, a stud, which fits the taper hole in the work spindle and the hole in the counterbore, is required.

*Grinding Milling Cutters or Metal Slitting Saws from 8 to 12
Inches in Diameter.*

Fig. 159 is a plan showing the 3-inch emery wheel, the saw or
cutter, the horizontal swivel and the tooth rest No. 3 in position

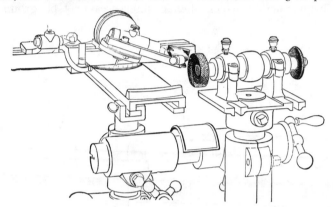

FIG. 157.—GRINDING SHELL COUNTERBORES.

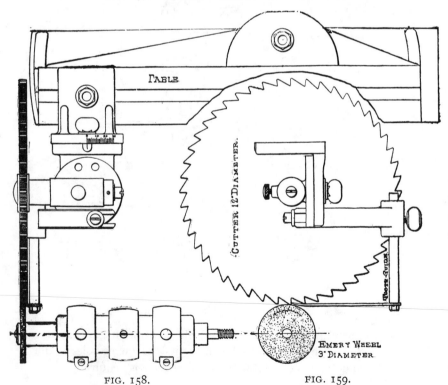

FIG. 158.   FIG. 159.

GRINDING MILLING CUTTERS OR METAL SAWS OF LARGE DIAMETERS.

for grinding, while Fig. 158 shows an elevation of Fig. 159, showing the long slide at the rear of the column end parallel to the emery wheel spindle, the universal head at the tail stock end of the
table, the saw held by work spindle alone, and the 3-inch emery
wheel on the left of the wheel head. The saw is clamped to the
work spindle by means of the long screw with nut and collar for
that purpose.

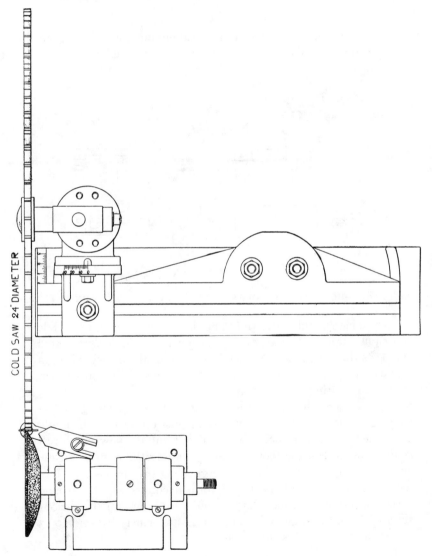

COLD SAW 24″ DIAMETER

FIG. 160.—GRINDING A COLD SAW, 24 INCHES IN DIAMETER.

Directions: Set the plane of the centers below the spindle plane the distance required for clearance. Set both swivels and table at zero.

Large saws, up to 24 inches in diameter, such as are used in cold saw cutting-off machines, are ground as shown in Fig. 160. It will be noticed that the universal head is here reversed on the table and the tooth rest placed on the emery wheel head.

Gear Cutter Grinding.

Figs. 161 and 162 represent an elevation and plan of the gear-cutter grinding attachment. The platen which holds cutter is fitted to the slot in the table and clamped to it by bolt and nut.

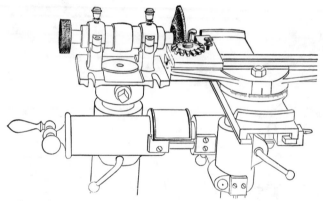

FIG. 161.—ELEVATION OF GEAR CUTTER GRINDING ATTACHMENT.

The table should be set right angular to the slide and the slide at a right angle to the axis of the emery wheel spindle (see dotted lines), as this position brings only the edge of the emery wheel in contact with the work, permitting a heavy cut to be taken without danger of heating.

In adjusting the cutter for grinding, the centering gage belonging to the attachment is set over against the face of the tooth. Then the pawl holder is clamped so as to bring the pawl tooth rest against the heel of the tooth. After swinging the centering gage out of the way, as shown in cut, the grinding may proceed. Thus, with this arrangement, gear and formed cutters can be ground correctly and in less time than by hand. Bushings for the various sizes of holes in standard gear cutters and emery wheel No. 3 are required with this attachment.

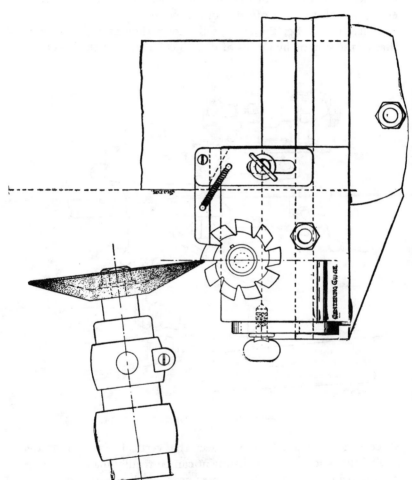

FIG. 162.—PLAN OF GEAR CUTTER GRINDING ATTACHMENT.

Grinding Formed Cutters.

Fig. 163 shows the table and long slide on the right of the column, the dish-shaped wheel on the right-hand end of the spindle, the two arms by means of which the center of the cutter may be held below the top of the table and the tooth rest No. 5 which engages with the heel of the tooth to be ground.

Directions: Set the axis of the long slide at right angle to that of the spindle by means of dial on column. Set the lower line

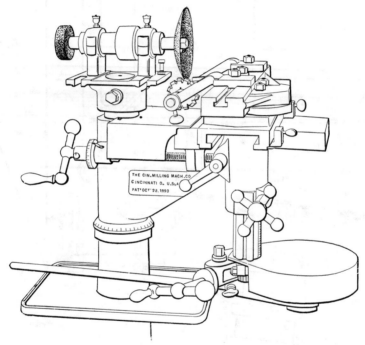

FIG. 163.—GRINDING A FORMED CUTTER.

of centers so that it will intersect the vertical diameter at the side of the wheel. This adjustment can be readily made by bringing the point of the tail stock center nearly·in line with the side of a straight edge held vertically against the flat side of the wheel. Put the cutter on a mandrel between centers and set the face of a tooth against the side of the wheel, making an allowance for amount to be ground off. To hold the face in this position, adjust tooth rest No. 5 to the heel of the tooth. Determine the depth of cut by short slide.

How to Grind a Worm Wheel Hob.

Fig. 164 shows the long slide on the left of the column, the special attachment on the table for holding the mandrel, the disk-shape wheel No. 3 on the left-hand end of the spindle and the table in line with the long slide.

Directions: See those given for grinding formed cutters.

Grinding a Hand Reamer.

Fig. 165 shows the long slide on the left, the cup-shape wheel

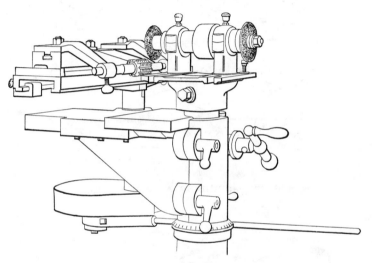

FIG. 164.—GRINDING A WORM WHEEL HOB.

on the left-hand end of spindle and the tooth rest No. 1 fastened to the top of the table.

Directions: Set the tooth rest below plane of centers a sufficient distance for clearance when grinding straight reamers. Set the table to grind straight. To grind bevel on end of reamer set table to angle required, or as shown in Fig. 166.

Grinding a Taper Reamer.

Fig. 167 shows the long slide at the rear right of emery wheel head, the table set obliquely to the side, the swivels at zero, the reamer between dead centers, a flat wheel at the right-hand end of the spindle and the tooth rest No. 3 fastened to the swivel.

Directions: Set the tooth rest in the plane of centers. Set

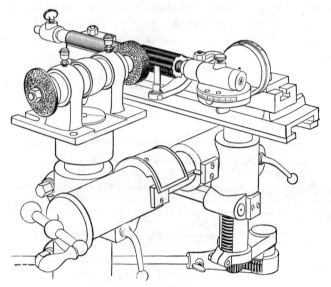

FIG. 165.—GRINDING A HAND REAMER.

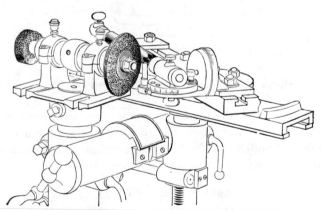

FIG. 166.—GRINDING BEVEL ON END OF REAMER.

the plane of centers below the plane of spindle the distance required for clearance. Set the table at the angle required for taper.

How to Grind a Hardened Drilling Jig Bushing.

Fig. 168 shows the emery wheel spindle with flat wheel on the right, the long slide on the right to the rear of the machine, the table set at zero, the grooved pulley running loose on the work spindle, which is locked by a knurled screw, the jig bushing on a mandrel held between dead centers and turned by a dog engaging with the grooved pulley.

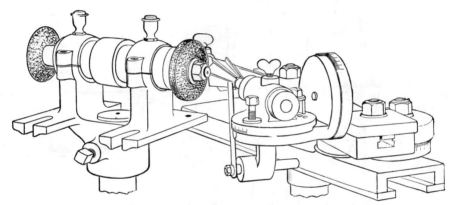

FIG. 167.—GRINDING A TAPER REAMER.

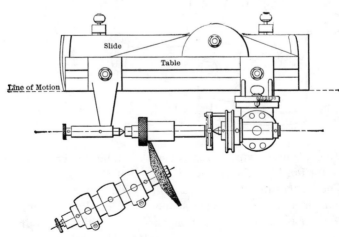

FIG. 168.—GRINDING A HARDENED JIG BUSHING.

How to Grind a Taper Spindle.

Fig. 169 shows the long slide at the back of the column, the wheel on the right of the spindle, the table set for the required taper, and the grooved pulley running loose on the work spindle. In circular grinding when the piece is held by the work spindle alone the grooved pulley is locked to the spindle.

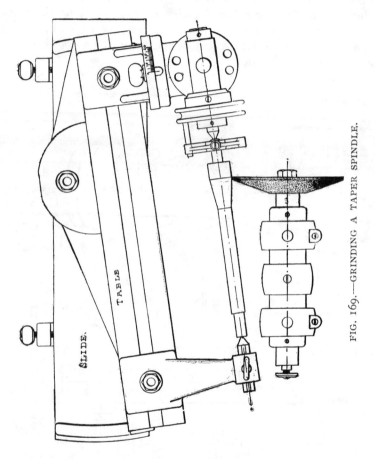

FIG. 169.—GRINDING A TAPER SPINDLE.

Emery wheel shape No. 3 is used for taking deep cuts; shape No. 5 for finishing the surface.

The centers in work that has to be ground must be very carefully made and held to proper shape. Hardened pieces must have centers lapped as nearly round as possible in order to obtain good results.

How to Grind a Slitting Knife with Beveled Edges.

Fig. 170 shows the wheel on the right of the emery wheel head, the long slide and table at the back of the column, the horizontal swivel set at the angle required by the face of the knife,

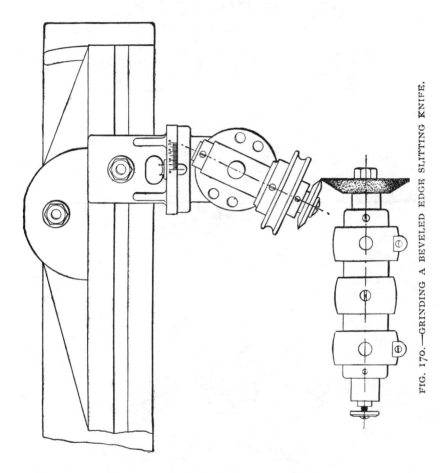

FIG. 170.—GRINDING A BEVELED EDGE SLITTING KNIFE.

the grooved pulley locked to the work spindle which holds the knife by bushing and long screw.

Internal Grinding.

Fig. 171 shows the long slide and table at the rear of the column and parallel to the spindle of the emery wheel; the piece to be ground is fastened to the work spindle, the internal grinding

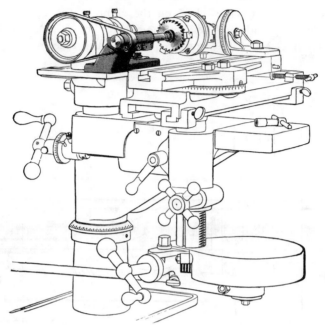

FIG. 171.—INTERNAL GRINDING.

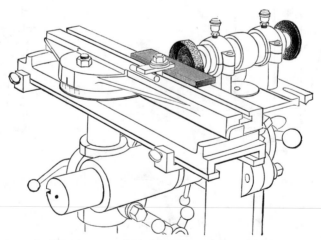

FIG. 172.—GRINDING A STRAIGHT EDGE.

attachment is fastened to the emery wheel head, with its pulley belted to the pulley on the right of the column.

Grinding a Straight Edge.

Fig. 172 shows the long slide on the left and parallel to the

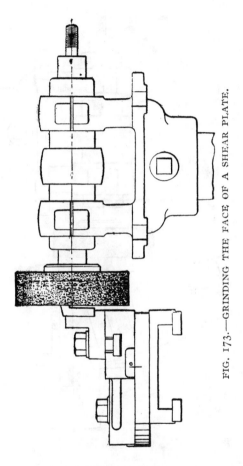

FIG. 173.—GRINDING THE FACE OF A SHEAR PLATE.

table, the straight edge clamped to its place, and a cup-shape wheel on the left of the spindle.

Grinding a Shear Plate.

Fig. 173 is an elevation showing on the left parallel to the table, the cup-shape wheel on the left and the shear plate clamped to the table.

How to Grind a Die Blank to the Required Angle.

Fig. 174 shows the long slide on the left, the table across the slide, the vise in the place of the universal head, the cup-shape

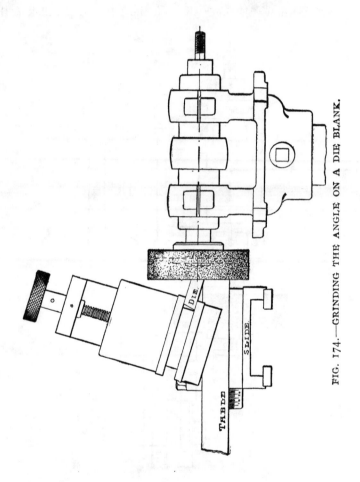

FIG. 174.—GRINDING THE ANGLE ON A DIE BLANK.

wheel on the left, and the vise turned on its pivot to the required angle.

Grinding a Formed Tool on Its Face.

Fig. 175 shows the long slide on the left, the table set at zero, the cup-shape wheel on the left of the emery wheel head, the vise set at 90 deg. for convenience in holding a screw machine form tool when grinding its face.

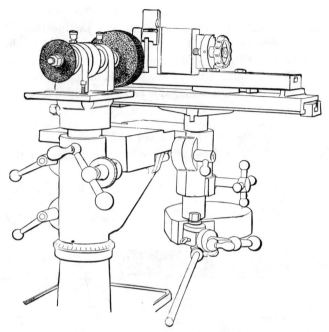

FIG. 175.—GRINDING THE FACE OF A FORMED TOOL.

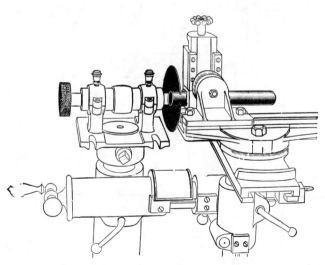

FIG. 176.—CUTTING OFF WITH THE EMERY WHEEL.

The Emery Wheel Used as a Metal Saw.

The engraving, Fig. 176, shows the vise on the table in the place of the universal head, the long slide at the right of the column, the table across the slide, and a wheel on the right of the spindle 1-16 inch thick and 8 inches in diameter. Brass tubing and small steel bars can be readily and smoothly cut into pieces by means described.

Grinding a Gage to a Given Dimension.

Fig. 177 is a plan view showing the long slide on the left,

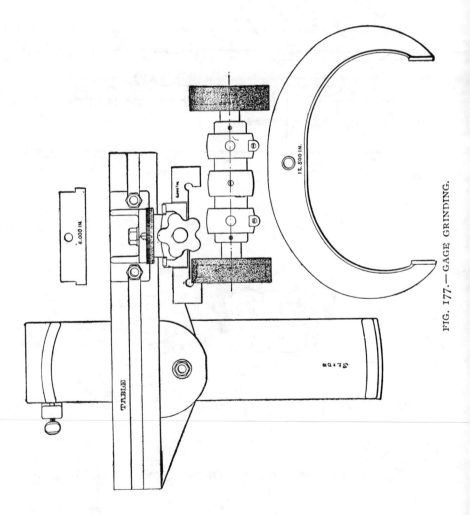

FIG. 177.— GAGE GRINDING.

the table across the slide, the vise in place of the universal head, the gage with one of its faces against the cup-shaped emery wheel on the left.

Attachment for Surface Grinding.

The attachment shown in Fig. 178 includes the vise shown, with angle and emery wheel No. 4.

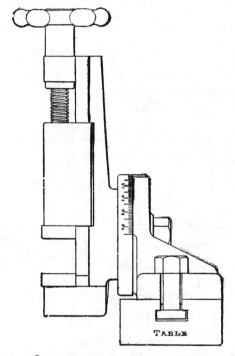

FIG. 178.—SURFACE GRINDING ATTACHMENT.

The vise may be clamped to the table at any point in its length.

Work held in its jaws can be presented at any angle whatever in regard to the axis of the emery wheel head, by making suitable adjustment of the swivel vise, the table and the long slide.

It has a graduated arc to measure the angle of elevation or depression at which the work is presented to the side of the emery wheel.

*How to Grind Milling Cutters and Metal-Slitting Saws Straight
or Concave.*

Fig. 179 shows the emery wheel head with a wheel on the
right, the long slide and table parallel to the emery wheel spindle,

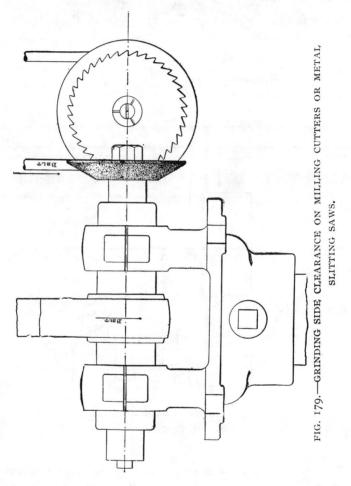

FIG. 179.—GRINDING SIDE CLEARANCE ON MILLING CUTTERS OR METAL SLITTING SAWS.

the horizontal swivel set at 90, and the saw fastened to work
spindle.

The round belt should be as loose as possible.

General Directions.

Hold the cutter to the tooth rest by hand.

In all cases when it is possible, limit the movement of the

long slide by the stops furnished for the purpose, for the following reasons:

It prevents the wheel from striking the head stock or cutter in concave grinding.

It prevents the wheel from running too deep into formed cutters and side milling cutters when grinding radial teeth.

It prevents the cutter from passing off the tooth rest, besides being convenient in quite a number of other instances occurring in the use of the grinder.

It is convenient and sometimes necessary in grinding cutters for clearance on the right-hand end of the emery wheel spindle, to swing the knee on the column to the right at an angle of from 5 to 15. This applies especially in angle cutters and small cylindrical cutters, when the belt is liable to strike the cutter or center.

After cutters have been reground once or twice the land becomes thick; it is very convenient under these conditions to swing the knee slightly around the column 2 or 3 degrees, and grind with a heavy broad cut between the teeth so as to reduce the amount of the land.

After the land is reduced to the proper width a slight movement of the knee back about 1 degree will alter the angle of the cut in such a way as to produce a narrow land with a keen cutting edge without danger of drawing temper.

The life of a cutter by this means is very much prolonged.

In using the lever or screw feed handles, adjust them by means of the clamp screws at bottom of long slide holder to the most convenient position.

Use the centering gage for determining the relative height of center of emery wheel spindle and tail stock center.

Diamond Tool Holder.

In order to obtain a good cutting edge and make a smooth finish on work, the emery wheel on a universal cutter and tool grinder must run true and have its cutting surface parallel with the movement on the slide of the machine. The cut, Fig. 180, shows a diamond tool and holder for truing emery wheels. This tool is made to be used either by hand or clamped to the table of the machine so that the diamond can be passed across the wheel in line with the slide in any position. It is absolutely necessary to have the wheel *perfectly true* on work ground between centers.

The proper use of this device will greatly increase the efficiency of any universal cutter and tool grinder, both as to quantity and quality of work produced.

A Small Cutter Grinder.

The small "Garvin" cutter grinder shown in Figs. 181 to 183

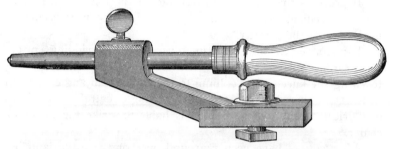

FIG. 180.—DIAMOND TOOL HOLDER FOR WHEEL TRUING.

has ample capacity for all the ordinary sizes and varieties of milling cutters, while its compactness and small cost render it practicable to have several distributed around in the vicinity of

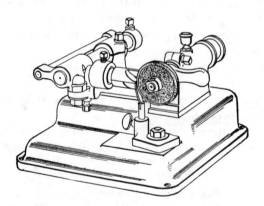

FIG. 181.—GRINDING A HOLLOW MILL.

each group of milling machines, where they will prove a valuable addition to the plant and soon pay for themselves in time saved.

The machine is well made throughout, and will grind straight or spiral mills and shell reamers from five inches diameter and four inches face down to the smallest side or face mills; bevel or angle-cutters from eight inches down; hand, machine, rose and taper reamers, as large as one and one-half inches diameter and eight inches long; butt mills, either straight or taper; cutters for milling T-slots, and hollow mills, such as used on screw-machines; saws, cutters for gear teeth, drills, and all such tools as are generally ground by hand can also be handled. Both spindle and arbor are of steel, hardened and ground, the latter to one

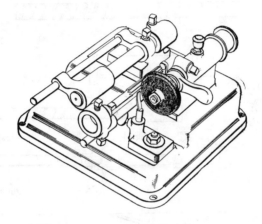

FIG. 182.—GRINDING A HAND REAMER.

inch standard size. All adjusting screws and nuts are case-hardened and fit wrench attached to the machine. The machine can be placed on the bench where most convenient and driven by straight or quarter-turned belt.

The spindle is provided with an eccentric adjustment for feeding the wheel against the work.

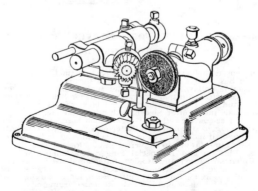

FIG. 183.—GRINDING AN ANGULAR CUTTER.

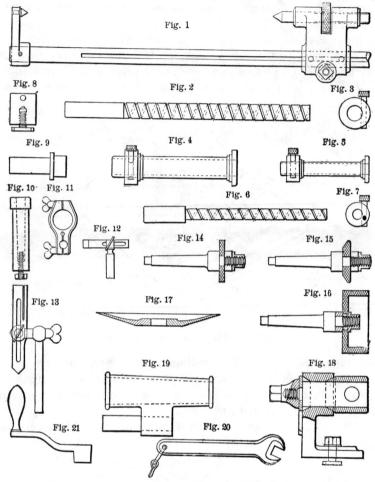

FIG. 184.—ATTACHMENTS FOR "GARVIN" UNIVERSAL CUTTER
AND TOOL GRINDER.

Fig. 1. Reamer Centers, holding work three inches in diameter, and at any length up to
eighteen inches. Fig. 2. Three-quarter inch Cutter Arbor. Fig. 3. Three-quarter
inch Adjustable Collar, for three-quarter inch arbor. Fig. 4. Three-quarter inch
Cutter Sleeve, with adjustable stepped collar, for holding cutters of one, one and
one-eighth and one and one-quarter inch bore, of any length up to five inches.
Fig. 5. One-half inch Cutter Sleeve, with adjustable stepped collar, for cutters of
five-eighth, three-quarter and seven-eighth inch bore, and up to three and one-half
inches long. Fig. 6. One-half inch Cutter Arbor. Fig. 7. One-half inch Adjustable
Collar, for one-half inch arbor. Fig. 8. Face Mill Stud, to be used on grinding table.
Fig. 9. Cutter Stud, for use in universal head. Fig. 10. Socket, for grinding small
end mills. Figs. 11 and 12. Special Finger Attachment, for grinding end mills.
Fig. 13. Universal Finger and Holder, for general use. Figs. 14, 15 and 16. Three
Arbors, with three styles of emery wheels. Fig. 17. Large emery wheel, for rear
end of spindle. Fig. 18. Universal Cutter Head, for use on the grinding table. Fig.
19. Arbor Socket. This socket is fitted with the Garvin and B. & S. taper. Fig. 20.
The only wrench used on the machine. Fig. 21. Crank Wrench, for the grinding
table.

Illustrations Showing Various Work Performed on a Different Type of Universal Cutter and Tool Grinder.

In the following pages will be found a series of illustrations showing some of the many kinds of work for which a Garvin universal cutter and tool grinder is adapted, also showing how to set the machine for doing this work. As a decided advantage over some machines, one can grind all work (except small-end mills) with the universal finger holder attached to and adjustable with the extended spindle-bearing, thus avoiding the accurate adjusting of the cutter-tooth with the line of feed, which is essential where the finger, or tooth-rest, moves with the work. This construction also permits of a very fine adjustment of the finger, which is obtained by slightly loosening the clamp and gradually swinging the entire finger-holder away from, or in toward the wheel, thus obtaining a greater or less amount of backing-off to the teeth, as may be required.

In all cases the face of the finger should be placed parallel with the tooth of the cutter and point against the direction of the wheel, as the spindle is run in one direction only.

When using the finger the stops on the grinding-table should be set so as not to allow the tooth to pass out of engagement with the finger. At the beginning of the stroke the tooth should only engage with the spring-pawl of the finger, which will allow the cutter to be turned around.

Fig. 185. Grinding the sides of face or straddle mills. The

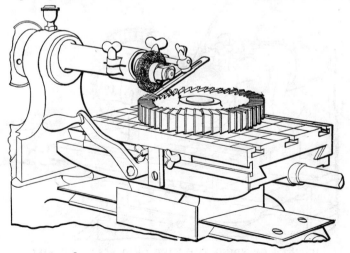

FIG. 185.—GRINDING SIDE OF A STRADDLE MILL.

cutter is held directly on the table and revolved on the face mill stud (Fig. 8).

Fig. 186. Grinding the reverse side of the same face mill;

FIG. 186.—GRINDING THE REVERSE SIDE OF A STRADDLE MILL.

no change in adjustment has been made, only the sliding platform has been moved on the knee.

Fig. 187. Grinding the face of a straddle mill, carried on a stud in the universal cutter head (Figs. 9 and 18); the grinding table being locked.

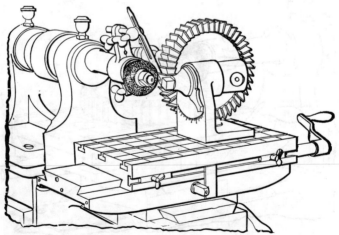

FIG. 187.—GRINDING THE FACE OF A STRADDLE MILL.

Fig. 188. Grinding a spiral tooth-cutter, carried on one of the sleeves (Figs. 4 or 5) which is made to slide on the arbor between the head and the adjustable collar; the grinding table locked by gib binder.

Fig. 189. Grinding a bevel cutter, placed on the cutter-stud (Fig. 9); clamped at the proper angle in the universal cutter head; the table moved between stops.

FIG. 188.—GRINDING A SPIRAL TOOTH CUTTER.

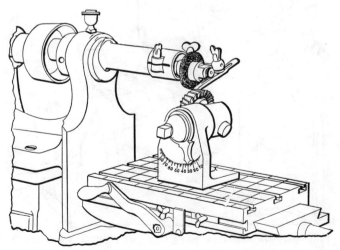

FIG. 189.—GRINDING A BEVEL CUTTER.

Fig. 190.   Sharpening a tap held in the reamer centers, which are carried in the universal cutter head.

Fig. 191.   Grinding a taper reamer in a manner which procures a straight backing off to the teeth.

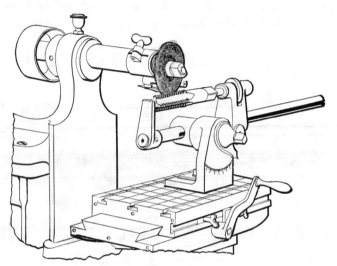

FIG. 190.—SHARPENING A TAP ALONG ITS FLUTES.

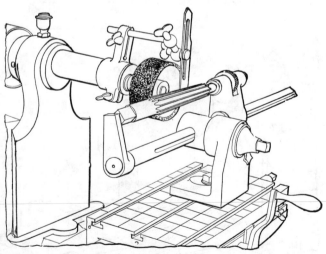

FIG. 191.—GRINDING A TAPER REAMER WITH A STRAIGHT
BACKING OFF.

Fig. 192. Grinding a taper reamer so as to produce a shear form of cutting edge.

Fig. 193. Grinding the face of a small end mill, held in the end mill fixture (Fig. 10) using the special finger-holder (Figs. 11 and 12).

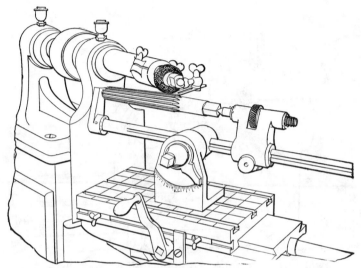

FIG. 192.—GRINDING A TAPER REAMER WITH A SHEAR
BACKING OFF.

FIG. 193.—GRINDING THE FACE OF A SMALL END MILL.

Fig. 194.   Grinding the sides of an end mill, using the same fixtures.

Fig. 195.   Grinding the face of a double end butt mill on its arbor and placed in the arbor socket (Fig. 19). A light application of oil will produce the proper tension in the socket.

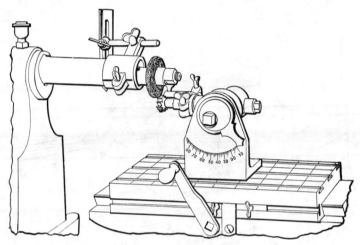

FIG. 194.—GRINDING THE SIDES OF AN END MILL.

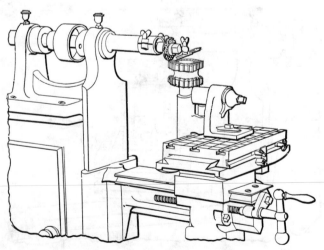

FIG. 195.—GRINDING THE FACE OF A DOUBLE END BUTT MILL.

Fig. 196. Grinding the bevel corner on a double end butt mill.

Fig. 197. Grinding a gang of mills without removing them from their arbor, which is placed in arbor socket (Fig. 19).

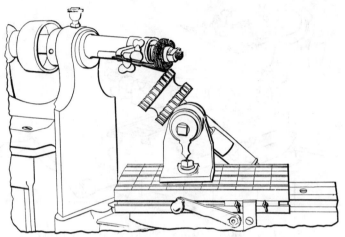

FIG. 196.—GRINDING THE BEVEL CORNER ON A DOUBLE END BUTT MILL.

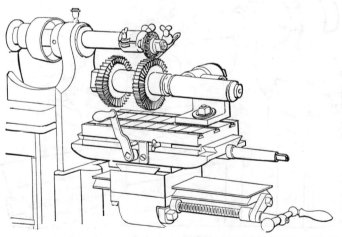

FIG. 197.—GRINDING A GANG OF MILLS ON THEIR OWN ARBOR.

Fig. 198. Grinding an inserted tooth mill.

Fig. 199. Grinding a die in its bolster bolted to grinding table.

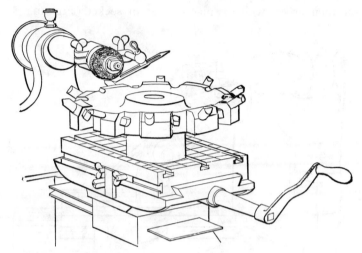

FIG. 198.—GRINDING AN INSERTED TOOTH MILL.

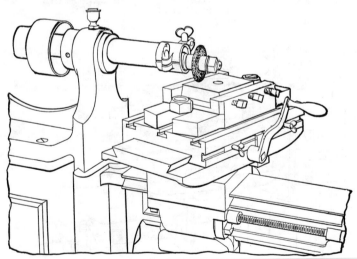

FIG. 199.—GRINDING A DIE IN ITS BOLSTER.

Fig. 200. Grinding a snap-gage in a vise bolted to the grinding table. All kinds of surface work, such as straight edges, snap

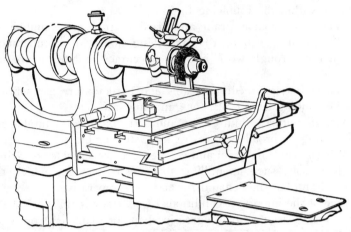

FIG. 200.—GRINDING A SNAP GAGE.

gages, punches, calipers, test blocks, etc., may be easily and quickly ground in this fixture.

Emery Wheels—Their Use.

The emery wheel consists of grains of emery and a composition called the texture which binds these grains together.

In regard to the size of the grains the wheel is said to be fine or coarse in grade. In regard to its texture it is called hard or soft.

To distinguish the grades, they are numbered from the dimension of the meshes through which the grains pass.

Thus grade 10 means that the distance between the wires of the mesh is 10 to the inch.

Some of the substances used to hold the grains of emery together are hard rubber, shellac, ordinary glue and a mixture of linseed oil and litharge.

The relative hardness of the texture is indicated by letters. Thus, A indicates a soft wheel; B, a harder wheel; M, medium wheel, and so on.

The vitrified emery wheel is made with a cement which contracts slightly while cooling, leaving small pores or cells through which water introduced at the center is thrown to the surface by centrifugal force. This flow of water operates to carry off the cuttings and the detached emery.

The grade and texture of the wheel in certain kinds of work is fairly within the following limits:

Wheels of coarse grain and hard texture are suitable for rough grinding such as the smoothing down of protuberances and in other rough work in which accuracy and finish are not required.

Wheels having medium grains and hard texture are serviceable in grinding lathe tools, for gumming saws, etc.

Wheels with medium grains and soft texture are suitable for free cutting on broad surfaces of iron, steel or brass.

Wheels with fine grain and soft texture are suitable for grinding fine tools, such as milling machine cutters for which the duty is light, but the demand for accuracy imperative.

One of the important conditions of accuracy is that the wheels vary in the least possible degree in shape or diameter from start to finish in a series of cuts.

The wheel with fine grain and hard texture is suitable for smooth grinding on soft metals such as cast-iron or brass.

A wheel glazes or gums if its grains are held too long by its texture.

The ideal duty of a wheel consists in having its grains displaced as soon as they become unfit for further service.

As the wheel in use wears out of true, it can be trued by a little black diamond point, and if very accurate grinding or a fine finish is required, the diamond should be carried across the surface of the wheel by the long slide.

If it is required to do heavy cutting, the emery wheel should be trued at a comparatively slow speed.

If the wheel becomes glazed, its surface may be improved by a coarse file or a piece of pumice stone.

Emery wheels should be kept clean and free from oil, and should not present more than 1-16 to ⅛ of an inch to the surface of the work. This provision is particularly applicable to cup-shape wheels.

If it is desired to put an exceedingly fine finish on such work as arbors, spindles, standards, etc., after they have been ground true, a wheel of 80 or 100 grade emery, with not more than ⅛ inch face, should be used for taking this finishing cut.

However, very finely finished surfaces can be obtained with a wheel as coarse as 40 grade emery, if the work is passed very slowly across the face of the wheel and the wheel allowed to cut but slightly.

In regard to finish, it is to be observed that the harder the substance to be ground the coarser must be the grade of the wheel.

Thus the finishing of steel requires a coarser grade of wheel than the finishing of copper.

If a wheel is too hard for the substance it is cutting, it may heat or chatter; this can be obviated somewhat by diminishing the width of the cutting surface, but it is much better to use a softer wheel and full width of cutting surface.

As a rule a soft wheel can be run more rapidly than a hard

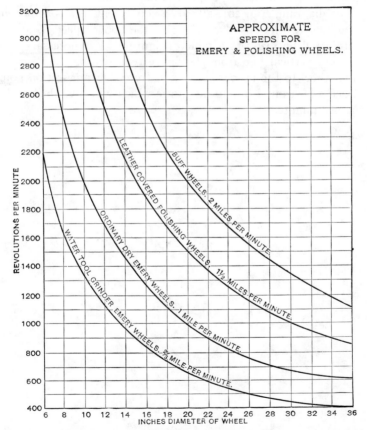

FIG. 201.—DIAGRAM FOR DETERMINING SPEEDS OF EMERY WHEELS.

one without changing the temperature of the work.   Accordingly there is an advantage in two speeds for the emery wheel spindle.

For internal grinding the wheel should be softer than for external grinding, and the work should revolve so as to give the wheel opportunity to do its work.

There can be no hard and fast rules for the speed of emery and polishing wheels since there is so great a variety in the nature of the work to be done, but a peripheral speed of about a mile a minute for ordinary emery wheels is commonly regarded as good practice. For water tool grinders the speed is usually about two-thirds that of dry grinders while on the other hand, polishing wheels are generally run at about one and one-half, and buff wheels at twice the speed of dry grinders.

The diagram, Fig. 201, affords a convenient means for determining the revolutions that will give the above speeds and will be preferred by many to a table of figures. It is necessary only to trace a vertical line from the figure representing the diameter of the wheel to the proper curve and from the intersection point to trace a horizontal line to the figure which will give the revolutions per minute.

TABLE OF ARTICLES MADE FROM CRUCIBLE STEEL, GIVING ABOUT PERCENTAGE OF CARBON THEY SHOULD CONTAIN.

A.

Carbon.

Arbor, saw	0.60 to 0.70
Auger, salt	0.70 to 0.80
Auger, wood	0.70 to 0.80
Axe	1.20
Axe, broad	1.15
Axe, overcoat	1.15
Axe, stone	0.80 to 0.85

B.

Ball bearing	1.20
Ball bearing plates	1.15
Back, butcher	0.80 to 0.90
Barrel, gun	0.60 to 0.70
Bits, auger	0.50 to 0.65
Bits, axe	1.10 to 1.15
Bits, channeling machine	1.15
Bits, jointer	1.20
Bits, mining	0.80
Bits, saw	0.80
Bits, scarf	1.22
Bits, tong	1.15
Bits, well, for stone drilling	0.80 to 0.84
Bits, artesian well	0.80 to 0.84
Bites, plier	1.00 to 1.10
Blade, table	0.70
Blade, knife	1.15
Blade, pocket	0.90
Blade, reamer	1.20 to 1.22
Blanks, milling cutter	1.15
Bolts, set	0.60 to 0.70
Bushing, spring	0.80

C.

Canes for hitting and missing devices on gas engines	0.80
Carriers, gun	0.60 to 0.70
Carver	1.00 to 1.10

Carbon.

Centers, lathe ....0.80 to 0.90
Chisels for cutting files......................   1.20
Chisels, chipping 1.10
Chisels, clay ....0.80 to 0.90
Chisels for hot work..........................0.60 to 0.70
Chisels, railroad track.......................   0.85
Chisels, blacksmiths' cold....................   0.85
Chisels, stone cutters' ....0.80 to 0.85
Chisels, wood working ....1.20 to 1.22
Chisels, brick ....0.60 to 0.70
Claw bars (pulling spikes) ....0.65 to 0.75
Cone, bicycle ....0.70 to 0.80
Creaser ....1.20 to 1.25
Cruciform, drill ....0.95 to 1.10
Cups, boiler makers' ....0.60 to 0.70
Cutters, flue ....1.20 to 1.25
Cutters, glass ....1.20 to 1.25
Cutters, milling ....1.20 to 1.25
Cutters, nail ....1.20 to 1.25
Cutters, corn stalk...........................0.80 to 1.00
Cutters, pipe ....1.20 to 1.20
Cutters, tong ....1.20 to 1.22

D.

Dies, bolt ....0.60 to 0.70
Dies, blanking (bottom dies)..................0.85 to 0.90
Dies, cartridge shell ....1.20 to 1.22
Dies, lever link ....0.85 to 0.90
Dies, cold heating 1.15
Dies, cutlery ....0.80 to 0.85
Dies, envelope 1.15
Dies, drop forging ....0.85 to 0.90
Dies, drop forging, for making table knives...0.68 to 0.78
Dies, hammer ....0.67 to 0.78
Dies, horseshoe (cold punching)...............1.20 to 1.22
Dies, glove ....0.85 to 0.90
Dies, nail 1.15
Dies, paper cutting 1.15
Dies, pipe ....1.15 to 1.22
Dies, rivet ....0.60 to 0.70
Dies, shoe ....0.70 to 0.80
Dies, silver spoon ....0.85 to 0.90
Dies, silversmiths' 1.15
Dies, tong ....1.10 to 1.18
Dies, wire drawing ....1.20 to 1.22
Dies for pointing machine.....................   1.15
Dies for manufacture of files.................0.67 to 0.78

Carbon.

Digging bars ....0.85 to 0.90
Dog, cant ....0.90 to 1.00
Drills for drilling tool steel shear knives.....................1.15 to 1.20
Drills for boring out shotgun barrels........................ 1.10
Drills, star 1.10
Drills, quarry ....1.10 to 1.18
Drills, twist ....1.20 to 1.22
Driver, screw ....0.60 to 0.70

E.

Edge, straight ....1.05 to 1.12
Expander sections ....1.20 to 1.22

F.

Facing, anvil ....0.85 to 0.90
Feather ....0.60 to 0.70
File, cabinet ....1.20 to 1.25
File, cant saw ....1.25 to 1.30
File, Great American cross cut..............................1.25 to 1.30
File, pillow ....1.25 to 1.30
File, slim taper ....1.25 to 1.30
Fork ....0.90 to 1.10
Fork, carver ....0.58 to 0.62
Furnace bars ....0.60 to 0.70
Flatters ....0.60 to 0.70

G.

Glut ....0.60 to 0.70
Grab ....0.70 to 0.90
Grips in tube works......................................0.85 to 0.90

H.

Hammer, bush ....1.25 to 1.30
Hammer, blacksmiths' ....0.67 to 0.78
Hammer, bush for granite.................................. 1.15
Hammer, machinists' ....0.90 to 1.00
Hammer, nail machine ....1.05 to 1.10
Hammer, peen 1.15
Hammer, pneumatic ....0.60 to 0.70
Hammer, ball peen ....0.80 to 0.85
Hardies ....0.60 to 0.70
Hatchet ....1.15 to 1.22
Hoe ....0.85 to 0.90

Carbon.

Holders, tool ....0.85 to 0.90
Hook, cant ....0.85 to 0.90
Hook, cant, for hammer dies...............................0.68 to 0.78
Hook, grass ....0.60 to 0.70
Hobs, for dies ....0.85 to 0.90

J.

Jar ....0.73 to 0.78
Jaw, chuck ....0.85 to 0.90
Jaw, gripping ....0.85 to 0.90
Jaw, vise ....0.85 to 0.90
Jaw for pipe machine 1.15
Jaw, wire puller..1.10 to 1.18

K.

Key for hammer ....0.75 to 0.80
Knife, belt ....0.80 to 0.85
Knife, blade 1.00
Knife, scarfing ....0.90 to 0.95
Knife, corn ....0.80 to 1.00
Knife, draw ....1.20 to 1.22
Knife, envelope ....1.20 to 1.22
Knife, hog 1.15
Knife, machine ....1.20 to 1.22
Knife, paper 1.15
Knife, pug mill ....1.05 to 1.10
Knife, shear ....0.85 to 0.90
Knife, whittler 1.15
Knife, wood working...1.15 to 1.20
Knife, carver 1.00
Knife, putty ....0.90 to 1.00
Knife, straw cutter...0.80 to 0.90

L.

Lining for brick dies...1.20 to 1.25
Links, valve ....0.60 to 0.70

M.

Magnet for telephones...1.10 to 1.17
Magnet ....1.23 to 1.25
Mandrel ....1.05 to 1.10
Mauls ....0.65 to 0.75
Mauls, wood choppers'...0.70 to 0.75
Molds, carbon ....0.87 to 0.95

Carbon.

Molds, brick ....0.80 to 0.90
Machinery, crucible ....0.55 to 0.65
Mattock ....0.60 to 0.80
Mower, lawn 1.00

N.

Nut cracker and pick.....................................0.70 to 0.73

P.

Pick ....0.70 to 0.80
Pick, mill ....1.20 to 1.22
Piercers for nail machine 1.10
Pinch bars...0.75 to 0.85
Pin, crank...0.55 to 0.65
Pin, eye...0.75 to 0.80
Pin, drift...0.60 to 0.70
Pin, expander..1.00 to 1.10
Pin, lever ....1.05 to 1.10
Pitching tool..0.80 to 0.85
Pivot ....1.05 to 1.10
Planer, stone ....0.70 to 0.80
Planer, wood... 1.15
Plates, guard..0.90 to 1.00
Plates for brick dies....................................0.85 to 0.90
Plate, throat, for hog...................................0.85 to 0.90
Plate, tool..0.90 to 0.95
Plow, crucible, for bicycle road scraper.................0.85 to 0.90
Plow, ice..0.80 to 0.85
Plug ....0.60 to 0.70
Plungers for bolt machine................................0.60 to 0.70
Plungers ....0.85 to 0.90
Pliers ....0.85 to 0.95
Point ....0.85 to 0.90
Point, clay pick...0.85 to 0.90
Point, piercing..1.40 to 1.50
Puller, nail...1.20 to 1.22
Punch, cartridge shell...................................1.20 to 1.22
Punch, hot work..0.85 to 0.90
Punch, file blank..1.20 to 1.22
Punch, skate blade.......................................0.85 to 0.90
Punch, washer..0.80 to 0.88
Punch, oil cloth...0.85 to 0.90
Punch, blacksmith..0.80 to 0.85
Punch, railroad track.................................... 0.85

R.

Carbon.

Racer, ball..0.90 to 0.95
Rake ....1.15 to 1.25
Reins, tong..0.60 to 0.70
Ring ....0.85 to 0.90
Rods, bench..0.66 to 0.76
Rods, piston...0.70 to 0.80
Rolls, expander...1.05 to 1.10
Rolls for hitting and missing device on gas engine.........0.85 to 0.90
Rolls, loom mill...0.55 to 0.65
Rolls for holding steel scrap on wooden shovel handles......0.85 to 0.90

S.

Saws, circular..0.80 to 0.90
Saws for sawing steel....................................   1.60
Saws, cross cut...0.85 to 1.00
Saws, band...0.68 to 0.75
Saws, drag 0.95
Saws, pit.... ....0.85 to 1.00
Saws, mill..1.25 to 1.30
Saws, gang...0.90 to 1.00
Scarf ....1.20 to 1.25
Scrapers, road..0.60 to 0.70
Scrapers, tube...1.20 to 1.22
Screws on elevators.....................................0.85 to 0.90
Screws, set...0.65 to 0.75
Sets, rivet...0.65 to 0.75
Sets, button ....0.65 to 0.75
Scythe edge...1.20 to 1.22
Shafts for skull cracker crane...........................0.60 to 0.70
Shafts, quick running motor...... ....0.55 to 0.65
Shear, pruning..0.85 to 0.90
Shear, sheep..   0.96
Shim ....0.60 to 0.70
Skate 1.15
Sledge ....0.65 to 0.75
Slides ....1.20 to 1.22
Snaps ....0.60 to 0.70
Spindle ....0.55 to 0.65
Spring, common locking..................................1.20 to 1.25
Spring, knotter...1.20 to 1.25
Spring, railroad..0.90 to 1.10
Spring, locomotive......................................0.90 to 1.10
Steel, carver...   1.40
Stretching bars...   1.27
Swages, saw ....0.85 to 0.90

T.

Carbon.

Taps	1.20 to 1.22
Taps, nut	1.15
Taps, spindle	1.20 to 1.22
Teeth, car wheel	0.85 to 0.90
Teeth, dredge bucket	0.75 to 0.83
Teeth, shovel	0.60 to 0.70
Teeth, saw	0.85 to 0.90
Tip	0.70
Tongs	0.90 to 0.95
Tongs, ingot	0.85 to 0.95
Tongs, skidding	0.85 to 0.90
Tool for turning hard rubber	1.05
Tool for reaming inside of guns	1.05 to 1.12
Tools, bricklayers'	0.90 to 0.95
Tools, blacksmiths'	0.60 to 0.70
Tools, moulders'	1.25 to 1.30
Trowel	0.40 to 0.45

V.

Vises	0.90 to 0.95

W.

Wedge, crucible	0.66 to 0.76
Wedge, stone	0.65 to 0.76
Wedge for breaking frozen ore	0.60 to 0.70
Wreath, crucible	0.66 to 0.76
Wrenches	0.80 to 0.90
Wrenches, track	0.80 to 0.90

INDEX.

288 INDEX.

Warming the work up to a blue... 153
Warped, straightening pieces which
    have 121
Warping, hardening a long punch
    so as to prevent 165
Warping, hardening very thin tools
    so as to prevent............ 158
Warping of long punches in harden-
    ing 171
Warping, of long tools in harden-
    ing 171
Warping, the weaker parts 101
Washington 178
Water and oil, hardening and tem-
    pering milling cutters in..... 147
Water, annealing 39
Water, cuts, lubricant for......... 196
Water for cooling 101
Water, kept at a boiling point.... 168
Weights and areas of round, square
    and hexagon steel........212, 213
Weights, measure of............ 211
Weight of cast iron, wrought iron,
    steel, copper and bronze..... 207
Weights of iron and steel sheets... 214
Weights of square and round bars
    of wrought iron 215
Weights and measures, United
    States 217
Weld which will not buckle or sepa-
    rate in hardening 163
Welding composition for cast steel.. 183
Welding cast iron 183
Welding, flux for soldering and... 187
Welding heats 175
Welding heat for steel should be
    higher than that for iron.... 175
Welding powder for iron and steel. 183
Welding steel to steel or steel to
    iron 175
Wetting the fracture 23
Wheels, approximate speeds for
    emery and polishing......... 267
When a muffle is used.......... 164
When hardening, dipping fluted
    reamers 157

When hardening, dipping half
    round or "gun" reamers...... 105
When hardening, dipping small
    tools 156
When the proper heat has been
    reached 153
When worn, increasing the size of
    the reamer 195
Whitworth, Sir Joseph 178
Why special instructions are given. 111
Williams & Co., J. H. 180
Wilson, Prof. E. 197
Without colors, to caseharden..... 130
Without heating, to blue steel..... 197
"Woodworker" 122
Work, cleaning the 135
Work, combination gas furnace for
    general machine shop........ 54
Work, hardening draw-bridge disc
    and similar 131
Work, laying out 196
Work, packing and heating the.... 129
Work, preparation of the 134
Work, packing the 45
Work, to dump the............. 135
Work, to pack the 134
Work with deep recesses........ 93
Working and hardening, suitable
    temperature of annealing,
    table of 127
Working Capital steel 21
Working up and down rapidly.... 154
Working steel for tools.......... 159
World's Fair, Chicago.......... 181
Worry, vexation and poor work.... 176
Wrenches, drop forged 189
Wrong, to apply the term "temper,"
    when it is 117
Wrought iron for crossheads, and
    crank pins 181

Z

Zinc, solder for 187
Zinc, to color or coat 206